# BERENSON

## and the Connoisseurship
## of Italian Painting

*A Handbook to the Exhibition*

David Alan Brown

National Gallery of Art, 1979

This catalogue was produced by the Editor's Office, National Gallery of Art, Washington. Printed by Schneidereith & Sons, Baltimore, Md. Set in Fairfield Medium by Composition Systems Inc., Arlington, Va. The text paper is eighty-pound Monadnock Caress with matching cover.
Designed by Melanie B. Ness

The exhibition dates at the National Gallery of Art are January 21-May 13, 1979

*Cover:* Bernard Berenson at Villa I Tatti, 1903. Villa I Tatti, Harvard University Center for Italian Renaissance Studies (see no. 6, Checklist)

*Frontispiece:* Bernard Berenson, 1909. Villa I Tatti, Harvard University Center for Italian Renaissance Studies (see no. 22, Checklist)

Library of Congress Cataloguing in Publication Data:·

Brown, David Alan, 1942-
Berenson and the connoisseurship of Italian painting.
Catalogue of the exhibition held Jan. 21-May 13, 1979.
Includes bibliographical references.
1. Painting, Italian—Exhibitions.   2. Painting, Renaissance—Italy—Exhibitions.
3. Painting—Expertising—Exhibitions.
4. Painting—Attribution—Exhibitions.
5. Berenson, Bernhard, 1865-1959.
I. United States. National Gallery of Art. II. Title.
ND615.B76     759.5′074′0153
78-27888

# CONTENTS

# FOREWORD

In its opening year, the new East Building of the National Gallery of Art has begun to serve many of the purposes for which it was conceived. Not only physically, but intellectually and conceptually as well, it is an integral part of the ongoing institution that is the National Gallery, an organism devoted not simply to the display of works of art, but to the furtherance of understanding about them.

Toward this end, the building will house a Center for Advanced Study in the Visual Arts, the outgrowth of a longstanding commitment to scholarship and research, particularly in connection with the Gallery's own growing holdings.

No part of the Gallery's collections is more important than its broad survey of Italian Renaissance art. The single scholar whose learning and discernment were most intimately connected with these pictures, in many cases long before there even was an American national gallery to house them, was Bernard Berenson.

"B.B.," as those of us who had the good fortune of studying with him were asked to call him, has become a legend. Even in his own lifetime, he was the subject of fascinated scrutiny in a full range of publications, from monographs to the *Reader's Digest*.

The presence of the National Gallery's collection under one set of interconnecting roofs has allowed us to take a look at Berenson in action. It is a study of his critical eye, and the critical traditions from which he sprang and to which he contributed. It is a look at Berenson and at connoisseurship. It is, also, part of a series of exhibitions designed to illumine various aspects of the National Gallery's collections.

The Bernard Berenson I knew, as a student, was a sage. Surrounded by books and beautiful objects in his villa near Florence, he seemed to stand for the wisdom of the past preserved in the present. His other activity, as a connoisseur of Italian painting, belonged to an earlier and less serene phase of his career. Coming twenty years after his death, this exhibition reassesses Berenson's achievement as a connoisseur. That such a project should be undertaken at all is itself a reflection of the resurgence of interest in connoisseurship, an interest not limited to scholars.

Because Berenson was able to clarify the work of major as well as minor artists, and in this capacity broke new ground, remaining problems of attribution have seemed less compelling to some scholars. Still there is a need, as there has always been, to make critical judgments about the art of the past and to discern what part of our visual culture remains of lasting importance. Present-day scholars in the field of art history may pay more careful attention than Berenson did to the ways in which history intersects with art, chiefly in the area of patronage and in the cultivation of taste, and to the subject matter in pictures. But the work of art itself, when examined in historical perspective, must always remain the fundamental object of study. In this sense connoisseurship is, perhaps, more of an approach than a method, an approach, moreover, that links the scholar with the ordinary viewer in the pleasure of coming to understand a work of art by looking at it. In Berenson's critical eye there is a lesson for us all.

This exhibition is unlike any previously held at the National Gallery of Art. It represents an attempt to display an intellectual process, as it was exemplified by Berenson. It has relatively little to do with biography. The exhibition is openly didactic. Berenson's choice and discernment were responsible for a great many of the Italian paintings in the National Gallery, of which some twenty have been included in the exhibition. They are complemented by more than one hundred drawings, prints, photographs, books, letters, telegrams, even a newspaper clipping. Though often beautiful to look at, the works of art here were chosen primarily for what they tell us about Berenson and the nature of the appreciation of Italian painting. To grasp the overall purpose of the exhibition, it is essential to realize that it is, in a way, not limited to what is on view in the exhibition itself in the East Building; it continues, we might say, among the early Italian pictures on permanent display in the main floor galleries of the West Building. For example, one masterpiece there, which Berenson came back to again and again, is the tondo, or circular panel, of the *Adoration of the Magi* in the Kress Collection. Berenson's efforts to reach a solution for its difficult

# ACKNOWLEDGMENTS

problems of attribution and dating involve two of the greatest painters of the early Renaissance in Florence, Fra Angelico and Fra Filippo Lippi.

We are grateful to the many lenders to the exhibition, among whom we wish to thank especially Dr. Cecil Anrep, literary executor of Berenson's papers, who kindly made the archives at I Tatti accessible. Craig Hugh Smyth, director of I Tatti, now the Harvard University Center for Italian Renaissance Studies, was also most cooperative, as was Dottoressa Fiorella Superbi, photograph librarian there. Mary Berenson's granddaughter, Mrs. Barbara Strachey Halpern, kindly agreed to lend three notebooks to the exhibition. Richard and Jaynie Anderson Pau of Oxford helped to secure the Morelli drawings, belonging to his descendants in Bergamo. The executive vice-president of the Kress Foundation, Mary M. Davis, offered assistance with the Kress material too. We are especially fortunate in having had the support of John Walker, director emeritus of the National Gallery, who, as Berenson's disciple, made personal the link between him and the Gallery.

Our particular appreciation goes to David Alan Brown, the Gallery's curator of early Italian paintings, who organized the exhibition and wrote the handbook accompanying it. Mr. Brown also enjoyed the assistance of many staff members who contributed in various important ways to the exhibition. Mrs. Fern Rusk Shapley, Berenson's onetime assistant and a former curator at the Gallery, has been most helpful with sound advice. To them and the representatives of all the other departments at the Gallery who were involved in such an undertaking go our grateful thanks.

J. CARTER BROWN
*Director*

Among the many staff members who contributed to the exhibition, special thanks are due to Barbara Murek for taking on unusual responsibilities during my research leaves, to Polly Roulhac for greatly improving the text of the handbook, to Gaillard Ravenel and Mark Leithauser for giving clarity in their installation to the diverse material in the exhibition, and to Kent Lydecker for organizing the audiovisual program.

D. A. B.

9

# INTRODUCTION

THOUGH WORKS OF ART are seldom signed or documented, it is desirable for many reasons to know by whom they were made or to which school they belong. The connoisseur seeks to give such anonymous productions their place in the history of art by trying to establish their authorship on the basis of comparison with known works. Aside from attribution, the connoisseur is also concerned with the related question of authenticity, whether a work is original or a copy. By attributing or authenticating a work of art, the scholar gains an intimate understanding of it, one that he might not otherwise obtain. Still, attribution and authentication are not the whole of connoisseurship, which means to evaluate, and not merely to classify. Having satisfactorily "placed" a work of art, the connoisseur may go on to assess its quality or intrinsic value, again by comparison with other objects of the same kind.

The exhibition *Berenson and the Connoisseurship of Italian Painting* illustrates the history and methods of connoisseurship, specifically as it relates to early Italian painting, by focusing on Bernard Berenson (1865-1959), for more than half a century the foremost authority in the field. Visually self-educated through a lifetime of looking at objects, Berenson was averse to the study of art history, which he regarded as a form of pedantry, unrelated or inimical to the enjoyment of art. Indeed, by present-day standards he would scarcely be considered an art historian. Berenson investigated the art of the past, but as a critic might: to elucidate its tangible form rather than its historical function.

In doing so Berenson recognized that many works of art fail to get the attention they deserve unless they have first been attributed to an artist. "But for this trait of human nature," he said, "connoisseurship would at best be a form of sport . . . [it] pays its way by assimilating the isolated work of art to its kin, thereby giving it a clear title to the treasure of admiration and interest these have accumulated." As with the *Madonna* [1, illus.],* now in

1. Antonello da Messina, *Madonna and Child.* National Gallery of Art, Andrew W. Mellon Collection 1937

* Numerals in brackets refer to the Checklist.

the National Gallery, which he ascribed to Antonello da Messina because of its "homely but distinguished simplicity," Berenson lamented that the painting went unappreciated before he "discovered" it. In convincingly attributing it to Antonello, he invested the unknown with meaning by relating it to the known.[1]

Bernard Berenson was born in 1865, the son of a poor Jewish family that emigrated from Lithuania to America when he was ten years old. A youthful prodigy [2], he gained entrance to Harvard College, where he studied literature, graduating in 1887. After this formative experience, Berenson made his way to Europe, feeling, like some character in a novel by Henry James, that he was about to enter the most decisive period of his life. The trip was meant to prepare him as a literary critic by making up a deficiency in his knowledge of the visual arts. On his first visit to Italy in the autumn of 1888, he found his true vocation; enchanted by Italian art, he decided to devote his life to studying it. Four pioneering essays on the Italian painters of the Renaissance followed. They were accompanied by the famous "Lists" of those pictures that Berenson accepted as authentic. It is on these lists, as well as other writings, that his reputation as a connoisseur is based.

A colorful, even controversial figure, Berenson is also remarkable for the role he played in the history of taste and collecting, working as he did from a fascinating coincidence of talent and opportunity. By the early twentieth

11

century, American millionaires were beginning to acquire masterpieces—or so they hoped—of Italian art. Berenson stimulated and guided that interest

3. Garden façade of Villa I Tatti. *Smithsonian* magazine, copyright Dmitri Kessel 1978

and, as the leading expert, authenticated paintings for dealers and collectors. The financial rewards of connoisseurship soon enabled him to purchase Villa I Tatti, near Florence. There, in a great house [3, illus.], surrounded by formal gardens [4, 5], he combined a life of scholarship and elegant hospitality. Urbane in manner and fastidious in dress [6, cover], widely read and witty, dreading vulgarity and lacking a social conscience, Berenson sought perfection of the self in aesthetic sensibility.

More than any other scholar, Berenson cultivated the role of connoisseur [7, illus.]. Sir Kenneth Clark has recently described how Berenson made his long experience of careful observation look spontaneous.[2] He would gaze intently at a picture, tap the surface (to test whether panel or canvas), and then dramatically murmur a name. If the mystique of connoisseurship contributed to the aura surrounding him, by the time of his death in 1959 Berenson was also renowned as a sage, his aesthetic philosophy having reached a broad public through his late autobio-

7. Berenson at the Borghese Gallery, Rome, 1955. Villa I Tatti, Harvard University Center for Italian Renaissance Studies

graphical writings. Nevertheless, it is Berenson's activity as a connoisseur that remains his lasting achievement.

12

# BERENSON'S CONTRIBUTION TO SCHOLARSHIP, TASTE, AND COLLECTING

Berenson's most tangible contribution to scholarship was what he called his "library with living rooms attached [8, illus.]."[3] Villa I Tatti, as he conceived it, was meant to provide a congenial ambient of learning [9]—unlike the bustle of university life—where the scholar could find the solitude he needed to think and write. Berenson was not inclined toward teaching. Rather, it was through personal contact, as well as his writings, that he shaped the thinking of a generation of scholars. He never formed a circle, preferring instead to deal individually with his disciples. As a consequence, he impressed each of them differently. Lord Clark, who worked at I Tatti at one time, admired Berenson's humanistic criticism, and it is in this vein that Clark wrote and narrated the famous *Civilisation* series. Yet, his exemplary Leonardo monograph and the drawings catalogue on which it is based are equally indebted to Berenson's example as a connoisseur.[4] Berenson was a pioneer in another field of study that Sir John Pope-Hennessy then made his own: Sienese quattrocento painting. Pope-Hennessy went on to become the authority in attributing Italian sculpture that Berenson was for painting.[5] During the last decade of his life, Berenson bestowed his gift for visual analysis on yet another distinguished disciple, Professor Sydney Freedberg, who, however, has exercised it on later Italian painting.[6] Left by Berenson to his alma mater, I Tatti is now the Harvard University Center for Italian Renaissance Studies. It continues

8. Library at I Tatti. *Smithsonian* magazine, copyright Dmitri Kessel 1978

to function as a research center [10], maintaining an active fellowship program and sponsoring conferences and publications.

Berenson's contribution to scholarship also takes the form of published writings. The four essays on the Italian painters of the Renaissance that first appeared around the turn of this century are ordinarily ranked first among his scholarly achievements. This appraisal has gained support from the fact that Berenson occasionally belittled his painstaking and inconclusive labors as a connoisseur, leading him to exclaim, "How worthless an undertaking is that of determining who painted, or carved, or built whatsoever it be. I see how valueless all such matters are in the life of the spirit."[7] Though admitting that connoisseurship was an indispensable preliminary to any valid history of art, Berenson, haunted by a sense of failure, lamented that making attributions had prevented him from continuing as an art theorist.[8]

When asked why he never revised the early essays upon which his initial fame as a theorist was based, Berenson

replied that he could not tamper with a "classic."[9] Indeed the essays remain of considerable historical interest as documents of late-nineteenth-century aestheticism. However, their lasting value in present-day terms is determined by what they contain of criticism of individual artists, not art theory.

The first and least original of the essays is *The Venetian Painters of the Renaissance* [11], which appeared in 1894. The adulation of Tintoretto, for instance, comes from Ruskin, whereas the central theme—that Venetian painting embodied the secular spirit of the Renaissance—Berenson found in Pater. Of greater interest is the volume on the *Florentine Painters* [12], first published in 1896. Berenson had shifted his activity from the Veneto to Florence, and he had, moreover, changed his way of thinking about art. He believed that Florentine artists were preoccupied with form and movement in their works and that the "tactile values" they created acted as a stimulus on the observer's sense of touch. Though "tactile values," or plasticity, would seem to be a specific quality of Masaccio's style, Berenson applied the notion as a uniform standard of judgment to the whole school, reproving artists who failed to measure up.

Likewise, in the *Central Italian Painters* [13] of 1897, Berenson took a quality of a particular artist's style—in this case, Perugino's sweep of space—and extended it to other Umbrian painters. Umbrian "space-composition," like Florentine "tactile

13

values," was supposed to arouse "ideated sensations" on the part of the viewer. While the celebrated notions of "tactile values" and "space-composition" may well be valid for Masaccio and Perugino, they do not convincingly sum up whole schools of painting. Berenson's misguided ambition as a theorist led him to over-generalize about specific qualities of form he had accurately observed.

The last and longest of the essays, *The North Italian Painters* [14] of 1907, points up the strengths and weaknesses of Berenson's method. Since those artists mostly lacked what he took to be the essentials of painting, Berenson dwelt more on their individualities. "Sensitiveness to the charm of femininity," for instance, was Correggio's distinguishing trait. Yet despite its somewhat more catholic treatment of certain artists, the essay adopts a uniform and inappropriate standard for evaluating Milanese painting, which Berenson dismissed as mere "prettiness in art." Throughout the essay there is the sense that however correct, Berenson's observations lack force. They become footnotes to more general attitudes of praise or blame, rather than forming the core of a statement about an artist's style, taken on its own terms.

The four essays—collected as *Italian Painters of the Renaissance* in 1930, illustrated in 1952, and paperbound in 1968—remind us, as does his person, that Berenson was a figure of the late nineteenth century and remained so long after his colleagues had broken their ties with that era. They contain impudent and paradoxical statements worthy of Wilde: "Whether, then, we are on the look-out for eminent mastery over form and movement, as for great qualities of colour and mere painting, Raphael will certainly disappoint us." And though Berenson claimed to have discovered the notion of "tactile values" while looking at

works of art, his aesthetic theories are largely derivative and undeveloped.[10] Moreover, he was not above using them jocularly, as when he wrote Jacqueline Kennedy in 1952 that it would "life-enhance" him to see her again.[11] Berenson's real potential was recognized as early as 1898 by Roger Fry, who regretted that Pater "makes so many mistakes about pictures; but the strange, and for a Morelli-ite disappointing, thing is that the net result is so very just. What is wanted now in the way of criticism is someone who will make appreciations as finely and imaginatively conceived and take them into greater detail as well. Perhaps Berenson will get to this if he gets over his theories. . . ."[12]

The essential part of Berenson's achievement lies in his activity as a connoisseur. In his writings he

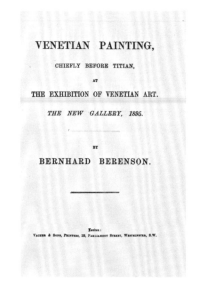

VENETIAN PAINTING,

CHIEFLY BEFORE TITIAN,

AT

THE EXHIBITION OF VENETIAN ART.

*THE NEW GALLERY, 1895.*

BY

BERNHARD BERENSON.

London:
VACHER & SONS, PRINTERS, 29, PARLIAMENT STREET, WESTMINSTER, S.W.

15. *Venetian Painting Chiefly before Titian.* Villa I Tatti, Harvard University Center for Italian Renaissance Studies

clarified artists' work by making significant attributions, precise visual analyses, and succinct definitions of what he called artistic personalities. He burst upon the field of connoisseurship in 1895. The occasion of his debut was an exhibition of Venetian art held at the New Gallery in Lon-

don. The objects displayed consisted mostly of paintings lent by aristocratic collectors whose attributions were adopted in the official catalogue.[13] Berenson, then only thirty years old, attended the exhibition and, appalled by the misattributions he found, was inspired to hastily publish a critical pamphlet [15, illus.], entitled *Venetian Painting Chiefly before Titian.*[14] To the consternation of the lenders, Berenson demonstrated that their attributions were incorrect, the polemical pamphlet thus placing him in the unexpected role of a cultural subversive.

The official catalogue listed no fewer than eighteen Giorgiones. Rejecting them all, Berenson said that the little *Holy Family* [16, illus.] for example, was by Giorgione's colleague, Vincenzo Catena. Though "Giorgionesque in outward characteristics as, for instance, in the drapery and colouring," the panel seemed, nevertheless, to lack the artist's "quality of magic."[15] As late as 1951, Berenson recorded this view on the back of a photograph. Soon afterwards, however, exercising the right of a connoisseur to change his mind, he came around to the Giorgione attribution favored today.[16]

Another painting that figured in the exhibition was Lord Pembroke's *Judith and Holofernes* [17, illus.]. Although of impeccable ancestry, having once belonged to Charles I, the picture was ruled out by Berenson as a Mantegna because of its apparently gaudy color and niggling execution.[17] He continued to doubt the painting, admitting that he found it more puzzling than ever. Nevertheless he included it as by Mantegna in the *North Italian Painters* of 1907.[18] Ten years later, the painting, purchased by the firm of Duveen, was cleaned and Berenson became more enthusiastic. He was not only convinced that it was autograph, he wrote to Duveen in 1916, but he found it superior to other works by the artist

14

16. Giorgione, *The Holy Family.*
National Gallery of Art,
Samuel H. Kress Collection 1952

17. Andrea Mantegna,
*Judith and Holofernes.*
National Gallery of Art, Widener
Collection 1942

in America. He regretted having been so hypercritical and afterwards consistently listed this enigmatic little panel as by the master.[19]

As a connoisseur the young Berenson was a revisionist, demoting pictures that, in some cases, he later upgraded. His work on drawings, though less controversial than changes of attribution, had a greater impact on art-historical methodology. In the study of paintings Berenson early learned to employ drawings, regarding them as evidence of a creative process that led to the finished work. His vast and innovative *Drawings of the Florentine Painters* [18] was already underway in 1896 and published in 1903.[20] Berenson later regretted the decision to undertake this monumental corpus. Nonetheless it remains his greatest single achievement as a connoisseur; no such systematic catalogue of drawings had ever been attempted before, and the text volume equally broke new ground by integrating the results obtained in the catalogue into a coherent picture of an artist's activity. The book, twice updated, has, like Berenson's other pathfinding work as a connoisseur, remained the standard reference in the field, impressive both for its extraordinary scope and for the subtlety of its judgments.

As for Berenson's achievement as a connoisseur of paintings, he similarly compiled a corpus called *Italian Pictures of the Renaissance* [19], published as a single volume in 1932. For each artist included he listed the works he accepted as authentic. How much Berenson added to our knowledge of Italian painting by means of attribution is not possible to assess here in any detail. It is clear, however, that he made a great many significant attributions.

A significant attribution is not necessarily one that we would take to be correct today. It is an attribution that was perceptive, given what was known about the artist at the time it

15

was made. The attribution should have pointed in the right direction, even if it did not turn out to be finally correct. It is not widely realized, perhaps, that few attributions are ever final. They are revised as the dimensions of our knowledge expand. Thus, the question sometimes asked of a connoisseur, whether he is (or was) right or not, ought to be rephrased to take into account the general state of knowledge at the time the attribution was made as well as the connoisseur's own understanding, both of which develop. A gifted connoisseur, Berenson transcended the limits of the knowledge of his time in numerous creative acts of perception about the authorship of works of art.

Berenson's contribution to scholarship consists not only of correct and significant attributions but also of precise visual analyses that are still worth consulting. He aptly compared Antonello's Madonna [1, illus.], for instance, to a "pyramid [rising] out of the earth." Today we would agree that the geometrical grouping of the figures and the way they dominate their space does indeed suggest Berenson's "pyramid."

A yet more important advance in art-historical methodology is Berenson's succinct definition of artistic personalities. Berenson went so far as to call connoisseurship the "sense of being in the presence of a given artistic personality."[21] This conception is original to him, his mentor Giovanni Morelli never having explicitly formulated individualities out of the characteristics he observed in artists' works. Personality so defined means the artist's creativity, not his biography. It consists not merely of the traits by which the artist is supposed to give himself away, but of essential qualities as revealed by his entire production. Berenson's innovative monograph on Lorenzo Lotto [20] of 1895 contains an account, which is a model of its kind,

21. Lorenzo Lotto, *A Maiden's Dream.* National Gallery of Art, Samuel H. Kress Collection 1939

of a painting [21, illus.], now in the National Gallery of Art.[22] Though Berenson misinterpreted the mythological subject, he was surely correct in seeing that the real interest of the picture lay in the "initial note of personality" it revealed. For Berenson this and other early works by Lotto had a "moral earnestness and a depth of feeling" that were unique for Venetian painting of the time.

We take this way of deducing an artist's intentions from his works for granted, but to grasp how new it was in Berenson's youth we need only compare other old monographs, where a hackneyed concept of an artist is imposed on his works. In Berenson's book on Lotto, the works themselves, rather than whatever happens to be known or believed about the artist, move to the center. The objects are of interest, though, not only for themselves but also for what they tell us about the artist who created them. Berenson thus characteristically focused on actual works of art as the object of his study. Even more than his writings, the example he set of a sensitive observer [22, frontispiece], endowed with a keen visual memory, may turn out to be his chief contribution to art history.

No less considerable than his contribution to scholarship was Berenson's role in the formation of American taste and collections. By the late nineteenth century, the Italian primitives no longer aroused controversy. Their appeal to collectors was that, together with the great High Renaissance masters, they belonged to a realm of art divorced from modern life. Nevertheless, in Berenson's youth there were, aside from the Jarves collection, practically no Italian paintings of importance in America. He regarded it his "mission to send [there] as many Italian works of art (and incidentally others too) as I could persuade collectors to acquire."[23] Aided by the Payne-Aldrich Tariff Act of 1909, which allowed for duty-free import of works of art over twenty years old, Berenson's success may be measured from the fact that there are now more Italian paintings in America than anywhere else outside their place of origin.

Berenson's start in what might be called applied connoisseurship dates from as early as 1890, when he wrote to his future wife Mary that he had "bought a picture for a friend. It was by Bronzino, a Madonna."[24] He further confided to Isabella Stewart Gardner, his first patron, that "advising about pictures is the path marked out for me. . . . I could sell ten times as much as I do now, if only I had a larger circle. . . . I want America to have as many good pictures as possible."[25] Berenson grasped that his career as an expert depended upon a coincidence of his talent with the opportunity that America offered. For, as Henry James observed, there was "money in the air, ever so much money . . . and the money was to be for all the most exquisite things. . . ."[26] Accordingly, in the autumn and winter of 1903-1904, Berenson and Mary, now his wife, traveled to America; the trip was recorded by Mary in a journal [23].[27] From it we learn that the Berensons sailed from Liverpool on September 30, returning to I Tatti some six months later, on April 4, 1904. Their purpose, broadly speaking, was to demonstrate how art "of fine quality ought to play a large part in the education of American taste" (November 9). They shared the task of promoting early Italian painting, Bernard reattributing pictures in public and private collections and Mary lecturing on connoisseurship at clubs and universities.

How frivolously the rich spent their money was appalling to the Berensons. Mary noted that a woman from Newport, where they were staying, had "had up all the organ-grinders and their monkeys from New York for a barrel-organ concert" (October 11). In Washington, where they liked the White House but not the Capitol, Mary went to see a "Botticelli," whose owner "meant us to stay for lunch, but when we wouldn't she insisted on showing me the gold plate I would have eaten off of if I had stayed" (February 18). The rich who bought art were scarcely better. A Boston collector "confessed he had no taste, but said he hoped to acquire it by indiscriminate buying" (November 23). In New York, the Berensons "saw the Havemeyer things—an awful Tiffany house!—Rembrandts, Monets, Degases ad infinitum—no real taste . . ." (March 3). The fact that late-nineteenth-century American collectors, even Mrs. Gardner, were acquiring what was then modern art, mostly French Barbizon and Salon painting, is difficult for us to appreciate, since until recently such pictures were banished from sight. The Berensons resolved to turn American millionaires toward the Italian old masters and, partly as a result of their tour, they succeeded as arbiters of taste in the fine arts.

As for providing the art, Mary Berenson—disarmingly straightforward—refers to dealing as an integral part of their program. They both "listened politely" to one possible purchaser (November 11), while she viewed the peculiarities of another "with a benevolent eye" (November 20). At dinner in Chicago, "as we stayed a while after the others, we talked about forming collections of pictures, and [their hosts] said they wanted to form one, but were afraid of the dealers. I think this was perhaps the most important thing for us financially we have yet met" (January 10).

In becoming an amateur dealer, Berenson followed a tradition that included such distinguished connoisseurs as Jonathan Richardson and Pierre-Jean Mariette in the eighteenth century and James Jackson Jarves and Morelli in the nineteenth. Scholarship always went together with collecting and dealing, we should recall, until the relatively recent time when art history became a well-established academic discipline. Berenson had contacts with emerging collectors, like Mrs. Gardner, and so he acted as a conduit to America for the "discoveries" made by him and his fellow disciples of Morelli.[28]

The Berensons' ambition centered on New York, which seemed a "Cyclopean San Gimignano" (December 4). "We watched it gradually light up [and] were awed and overcome by the vastness and grandeur of it" (December 10). Bernard "startled me," Mary added, "by asking me whether he should let it be known that he would be willing to succeed Cesnola as director of the Museum here. I saw a thousand advantages in it, but I also think it would be a waste of a man who can think. Today's visit there confirmed me. It is a vast collection of horrors." At stake was the Metropolitan Museum, whose accumulations were already outgrowing their quarters in Central Park.

While Bernard was angling for the directorship, Mary lectured. At Smith College she explained "How to Enjoy the Old Masters" (October 29). Mrs. Gardner attended another of Mary's lectures at Wellesley, "wearing all her jewels because she said she had heard of a butler who stole the jewels of his mistress during her absence" (November 19). An engagement at a Chicago club "gave some of the tired men whose wives had dragged them there a chance for a quick nap" (January 5). The following day Mary spoke at the Art Institute about "The New Art

Criticism" and soon thereafter to another club on "The Art of Portraiture Old and New" (January 8). After a stop in Buffalo (January 15), she repeated "The New Art Criticism" at the Pennsylvania Museum (February 6), comparing "scientific" connoisseurship to the detective work of Sherlock Holmes. Getting into her stride, she spoke in New Haven and Hartford on the same day (February 20). Then, after having been called back to Wellesley and appearing in Boston (February 27 and 29), she wrote "my Philadelphia speech, which [B.B.] had sketched out for me" (March 4). The subject was "Art Collections in America and their Influence on National Taste and Art" (March 8).

The Berensons frequented the more learned and discriminating collectors who met their approval: Marquand in Princeton (December 4-5), Freer in Detroit (January 13-14), and Johnson in Philadelphia (January 29-31, February 5). Their favorite, of course, was Mrs. Gardner [24, illus.], who, devoted to her museum, "lives very sparingly, wearing old clothes and eating almost nothing" (October 17). Though claiming that "all connoisseurs dis-

agree and so nothing can be known," Mrs. Gardner (1840-1924) had relied on Berenson to help form the collection newly installed in her Italianate palace in Boston [25].[29] Their cooperation made Isabella the first great collector (after Jarves) of old master paintings in America, and it enabled Berenson to gain the fame and fortune he sought. At Fenway Court, which remains almost unchanged today, the Italian paintings were displayed in a rich setting [26, illus.] of furniture

and decorative arts that evokes the Renaissance period. "In beauty and taste," Mary Berenson wrote, "it far surpassed our expectations, which were high. There is very little to find fault with. . . . The rest is too lovely to attempt to describe. One room is more entrancing than another, and the great masterpieces of painting seem mere decoration in the general scheme. I thought there was remarkably little that was not of Bernard's choosing, but that little annoyed him

26. Interior of Fenway Court.
Isabella Stewart Gardner Museum

27. Jarves Collection installation.
Yale University Archives, Yale
University Library

24. Isabella Stewart Gardner, c. 1905.
Isabella Stewart Gardner Museum

18

immensely and hurt him too" (November 14).

Reattributing pictures made the Berensons unpopular with museum officials. In New Haven, for example, they "rushed at once to the Jarves Collection [27, illus.]," then installed in Yale's School of Fine Arts, and "found a nice little roomful of pictures, some really good. . . ." (November 2). "We spent the [next] day taking notes on the gallery. It is an interesting one and there are 14 pictures we should gladly own." On November 4 Mary returned to the collection, "into which various natives were coming attracted, for the first time in their lives, by the sensation of having 'all the attributions authoritatively contradicted.' Professor Niemeyer came and gave me a long lecture, telling me that the 'Botticelli' [28, illus.] (an indifferent school piece) was the finest in existence, except possibly the *Birth of Venus*. He said he had copied it, so he knew far more about it than a person (like me!) who only looked at it could possibly know. There was no answer and I made none. His pretentiousness amused and horrified me, for no mat-

28. Follower of Botticelli, *Madonna and Child*. Yale University Art Gallery, University Purchase from James Jackson Jarves

30. Aerial view of Lynnewood Hall, Elkins Park, Pennsylvania. Historical Society of Pennsylvania

ter what out-of-the-way name I mentioned, he made as if he knew all about it—and of course he couldn't possibly. I did." Bernard and Mary carried with them an old manual of the collection [29], incorporating Jarves' views, and in it she duly annotated the "Botticelli" as "school—not one of the worst."[30]

Attributions change, and misguided collectors might be redeemed too. On January 27 the Berensons visited the Widener collection in Philadelphia, where they found "mostly horrors masquerading under great names." P. A. B. Widener (1834-1915), who began as a butcher supplying meat to Civil War troops, made an immense fortune in urban mass transit. And, like other self-made multimillionaires, he acquired works of art. These were displayed at Lynnewood Hall [30, illus.], a hundred-room neoclassical mansion built around the turn of the century in Elkins Park.

On another visit to America in 1908, the Berensons, J. P. Morgan

heard, were "going to Philadelphia to bust up Widener's collection."[31] They did spend two days there [31, illus.], in fact, finding "nothing of importance among their Italians. . . . We could not leave a single name. . . . It was rather touching to have old Mr. Widener trotting round and saying meekly, 'Mr. Berenson, is this a gallery picture, or a furniture picture, or must it go to the cellar?' He was very much pleased whenever we would allow a picture to stay in the gallery, even if shorn of its great name. But we had to banish several. . . . However, they're now determined to abide by the best expert opinion they can get. Whether they will buy any more or not, I have no idea, but what they have is going to be correctly named if possible."[32]

Joseph Widener [32, illus.], a real art lover (1872-1943), added to and refined his father's holdings so that by the time his bequest came to the National Gallery of Art in 1942, it was the greatest private collection in

31. Long gallery at Lynnewood
    Hall, at the time of Berenson's
    visit.
    National Gallery of Art

20

32. Joseph Widener.
    Culver Pictures Inc.

33. Raphael room at Lynnewood Hall, the result of Berenson's influence.
    National Gallery of Art

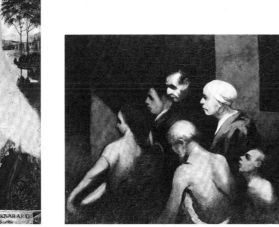

34. Neroccio de' Landi, *Portrait of a Lady*. National Gallery of Art, Widener Collection 1942

35. Honoré Daumier, *The Beggars*. National Gallery of Art, Chester Dale Collection 1962

36. Andrea del Castagno, *The Youthful David*. National Gallery of Art, Widener Collection 1942

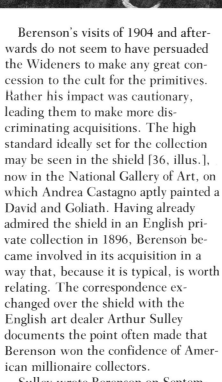

America.[33] He transformed the grandest of the Gilded Age estates from the tasteless opulence disapproved by the Berensons into a magnificent ensemble [33, illus.] of choice paintings, furniture, and decorative arts. Admittedly, the pseudo-Renaissance decor was inaccurate, but it was evocative all the same, and revealing of how highly the pictures were regarded.

On March 5, 1912, Joseph Widener wrote Berenson about "recent additions, the best of which, you will note, is that charming little portrait [34, illus.] by Neroccio di Landi. I think you saw the picture. . . . You really can't imagine how delightful the new galleries are, with the elimination of all unimportant pictures."[34] By chance, one such rejected painting is now in the National Gallery of Art. Having failed to enter with Widener's bequest, Daumier's *Beggars* [35, illus.] came, after taste had changed, as part of the Chester Dale Collection in 1962.[35]

Berenson's visits of 1904 and afterwards do not seem to have persuaded the Wideners to make any great concession to the cult for the primitives. Rather his impact was cautionary, leading them to make more discriminating acquisitions. The high standard ideally set for the collection may be seen in the shield [36, illus.], now in the National Gallery of Art, on which Andrea Castagno aptly painted a David and Goliath. Having already admired the shield in an English private collection in 1896, Berenson became involved in its acquisition in a way that, because it is typical, is worth relating. The correspondence exchanged over the shield with the English art dealer Arthur Sulley documents the point often made that Berenson won the confidence of American millionaire collectors.

Sulley wrote Berenson on September 15, 1912, that "the shield is ours, if we keep things quiet." By December 5 of that year, when he next wrote

about it, Sulley had purchased the shield and was considering taking it to America "to show to Mr. Widener. Do you think it would be good for you to write to him and explain how rare and desirable it is?" Berenson, who always refused to write collectors directly advertising dealers' wares, evidently demurred, for Sulley next suggested that Berenson write him instead (December 11). On the basis of the letter Berenson provided (December 24), Sulley "sold the shield to Mr. Widener. I, of course, showed him what you had written me about it. He asked me to write to you and tell you that he had bought it and to say that he would be glad if you would send him the manuscript for the catalogue relating to it as soon as possible" (January 15, 1913). Berenson's fine appreciation of the Castagno shield was included in the privately printed catalogue [37], sumptuously bound in red leather and lined in green silk, in which he surveyed the Wideners' Italian pictures.[36]

21

Undoubtedly the most enigmatic American collector of Italian primitives was Carl W. Hamilton [38, illus.]. Though he intended to be a missionary, Hamilton (1886-1967), after graduating from Yale, became a capitalist instead. His zeal, then, took the form of an almost Victorian enthusiasm for the spiritual value of art, long after

40. Domenico Veneziano. *St. John in the Desert.* National Gallery of Art, Samuel H. Kress Collection 1943

38. Carl Hamilton. Courtesy of Catherine Hamilton Lancaster and Rita Hamilton Hager, granddaughters

39. Carl Hamilton's apartment in New York. Courtesy of Catherine Hamilton Lancaster and Rita Hamilton Hager, granddaughters

22

taste had shifted away from religious subject matter. He acquired major early Italian paintings, several of which are now in the National Gallery of Art, including Mantegna's *Judith* [17, illus.]. The collection was displayed in an apartment [39, illus.], a "gloomy place in a skyscraper" at 270 Park Avenue in New York. Just as the Renaissance decor of his "super-museum" was inspired by I Tatti,[37] so Hamilton, an avid reader of the *Italian Painters of the Renaissance,* was cultivated as a collector by the Berensons. The phenomenal rise in picture prices had forced Mrs. Gardner out of the market for masterpieces, while the more fashionable collection of the Wideners favored the Grand Manner. Alerted to Hamilton's potential as early as 1917, the Berensons made his acquaintance two years later. On a visit to America in 1920-1921, they stayed with him, as they had with Mrs. Gardner some fifteen years earlier. Mary lectured on his pictures at Bryn Mawr and Harvard, while Bernard sat down to write no fewer than four articles featuring Hamilton's recent acquisitions.[38] Out of friendship, Berenson even offered advice about works that Hamilton was considering for purchase.

According to an often-repeated anecdote, Mary Berenson gave Hamilton a picture from I Tatti: Domenico Veneziano's *St. John in the Desert* [40, illus.].[39] Berenson, the story goes, regretted the loss of this rare and important little panel, which formed part of an altarpiece once in the church of Santa Lucia dei Magnoli in Florence. Nevertheless, as a letter [41, illus.], dated October 19, 1919, reveals, both Berensons presented Hamilton with the picture, presumably to encourage him as a collector. First a photograph and a promise reached him, and then the painting. "Here I sit before 'St. John in the Desert,'" Hamilton wrote, "completely charmed by it. It is more wonderful than I thought it could be even after B.B.'s enthusiastic and beautiful description of it. Never have

CLARIDGES HOTEL,
BROOK STREET. W. 1.

Dear B. B. and Mrs. Berenson,
Here I sit before "St John in the Desert" completely charmed by it. It is more wonderful than I thought it could be even after B. B.'s enthusiastic and beautiful description of it. Never have I received a present either so valuable or one which I have appreciated so much. Would that in some way I could

41. Letter from Carl Hamilton to the Berensons. Villa I Tatti, Harvard University Center for Italian Renaissance Studies

I received a present so valuable or one which I have appreciated so much. . . . I have never seen nude so chaste, and the composition and color of the picture together with the majesty and solemnity of the mountain peaks fill me with absolute satisfaction." Hamilton repeatedly thanked the Berensons for the picture, which was then attributed to Pesellino.[40] Only later did Berenson grasp that he had parted with a masterpiece by Domenico Veneziano.[41]

Berenson was also chagrined over the gift because Hamilton did not fulfill their expectations. Hamilton's appetite for art exceeded his ability to pay for it, and he was obliged to return some of his pictures, bought on credit, in 1921. Mary Berenson wrote Mrs. Gardner on November 25, 1922, that Hamilton "has been a real disillusion for us, for certainly he started collecting in a most unusual spirit, and he undoubtedly loved the pictures. We

hoped he would be one of the great collectors in the world. . . ." Hamilton eventually turned to the Berensons for help in disposing of the rest of his paintings, seeking authentications they reluctantly provided.[42] After being widely exhibited, the remainder of his pictures were sold (at a considerable profit) in 1929.[43] Hamilton only dabbled in collecting afterwards, prefer-

42. Samuel H. Kress, 1924. Samuel H. Kress Foundation

ring to spend his time and money on charity.

A chapter of American taste closed with Samuel H. Kress [42, illus.], a chain-store magnate who was the last great collector of Italian primitives. His pictures, ranging from the thirteenth through the eighteenth centuries, vastly outnumbered those brought together by Mrs. Gardner, the Wideners, and Carl Hamilton. For these latter collectors Berenson acted as advisor and agent, as he did for John G. Johnson (1841-1917) in Philadelphia, Henry Walters (1848-1931) in Baltimore, and Percy Straus (1876-1944) and Robert Lehman (1892-1969) in New York.[44] Berenson's relation to Samuel Kress (1863-1955), on the other hand, after their first meeting in 1936, and to his brother Rush (1877-1963) was that of a distant ally. The

correspondence they exchanged as old men deals mostly with the future of their legacies in a world they perceived as hostile to humanism. The regional distribution of the Kress pictures and the republication of Berenson's *Italian Painters* and *Italian Pictures* in illustrated editions, sponsored by the Kresses, were meant to regenerate the interest of the American public in traditional, as opposed to radical, values.[45] Even I Tatti was calculated to play its part as a research center by keeping "alive the interest in the great art of the past."[46] Only one work of art was discussed in the correspondence: the tondo of the *Adoration of the Magi*, now in the National Gallery, whose acquisition Berenson urged as a masterpiece by Fra Angelico and Fra Filippo Lippi.[47]

43. Giotto, *Madonna and Child.* National Gallery of Art, Samuel H. Kress Collection 1939

Berenson's authority was invoked to ensure the attribution and thus the efficacy of Kress paintings such as a *Madonna* [43, illus.] by Giotto which came to the National Gallery. Though at first he believed that the picture was by Giotto's pupil, Bernardo Daddi,

23

Berenson subsequently came out in favor of the Giotto attribution. The painting had, in fact, proved to be the central panel in an altarpiece by Giotto.[48] Berenson's change of mind was reported as a newsworthy event by the *New York Herald Tribune* on October 30, 1959. The article [44] shows the public perception of the significance of Berenson for establishing the status of works in collections such as the Kresses'.

In a telegram [45] of May 22, 1939, Berenson was asked to cable his estimate of the Kress collection as a whole. His support was solicited because the collection was about to join the smaller but finer one of Andrew Mellon in the National Gallery. In his draft of a reply [45] Berenson stated that "there are two types of collections, those like Widener, Gardner, Frick or Bache consisting of masterpieces only & those like Johnson, Philadelphia, constituting historical series. Stop. Kress combines both. Few Italian painters between 1300 and 1600 missing & the greatest represented by highly characteristic examples in excellent condition."[49] Berenson's remarks were quoted "in the public announcement of the Kress gift & with good effect, for the editorial writers quoted you, in much the same way as they cite an opinion of the Supreme Court!"[50]

Before coming to the National Gallery, the Kress collection was displayed in a Fifth Avenue duplex apartment [46-50; 49, illus.], decorated in Renaissance style, with marble and tile floors, carved chests and tables, and leaded glass windows. At first Samuel Kress bought indiscriminately, intending to form an exhaustive survey of Italian painting. Rush Kress was led by John Walker, with Berenson's advice, to improve that part of the collection destined for the Gallery. He also expanded the collection to include the non-Italian schools, without losing its

49. Samuel H. Kress apartment, New York. Samuel H. Kress Foundation

original character, however. The Kress collection was no more aesthetically adventurous than those of Widener or Hamilton. It aimed not to be avant garde but to elevate the taste and character of those who viewed it. Berenson, whose historic role was to demonstrate the formal beauty of early Italian painting, thus found himself advising a collector who prized the religious message in art. His moral bias links Rush Kress with James Jackson Jarves, who, a century before, had tried to form a comprehensive art collection that would be broadly educational.

Berenson's importance for the Widener and Kress collections, which came to the National Gallery of Art, has been described. Other Gallery paintings, including several donated by Andrew Mellon, once belonged, if only briefly, to Berenson's collector protégé, Carl Hamilton. In addition, as the present director, J. Carter Brown, has noted, the Gallery is more directly a "product of [Berenson's] eye and taste

than many realize, for during its period of rapid acquisition in the Italian field he was virtually an adjunct curator; and his vision, shared by John Walker, of an art museum as a company of scholars, will soon become a reality in the Center for Advanced Studies in the Visual Arts."[51] Before the West Building was completed, David Finley, the Gallery's first director, wrote Berenson, "I hope that, between us, John [Walker, then chief curator] and I can keep you informed about all we do. I cannot tell you how highly I value your advice and the interest you feel in our efforts to give this newly born gallery the right start."[52] The Gallery's Italian paintings, unrivaled in America for the earlier schools, might almost have been chosen to illustrate the *Italian Painters of the Renaissance*. Berenson's closest disciple, in fact, was John Walker [51, illus.], who lived and worked at I Tatti during the 1930s and who returned nearly every summer thereafter. Berenson even gave him a picture from his

24

51. Bernard Berenson and John Walker, in the garden at Villa I Tatti. Villa I Tatti, Harvard University Center for Italian Renaissance Studies

own collection, a *Madonna* [52] by the anonymous fifteenth-century Florentine painter known as the Master of San Miniato.[53]

Involved as he was with the art market, Berenson has been criticized for using culture as a commodity. By the same token, his activity as an expert has also been justified by its effect of bringing great Italian paintings to America. Both viewpoints fail to take into account his place in history. Berenson was, in fact, the last great representative of a type, the connoisseur-dealer. Along with most art historians of his generation, Berenson authenticated works of art. In that respect, as an agent, he found, bought, and sold paintings. He also advised on works offered for purchase by other sources and, in this capacity, was associated with a number of dealers, at first with Colnaghi's, then from about 1907 to 1937 primarily with Duveen Brothers. It was through the latter that Berenson served yet another collector for the National Gallery, Andrew Mellon; though he was not personally acquainted with Mellon, Berenson authenticated Italian paintings Mellon purchased from Duveen.

Berenson was an amateur, for whom authenticating works of art was a means of livelihood. As a young man, wishing to become a connoisseur of old master Italian paintings and drawings, he had been obliged to seek self-employment abroad. Unfortunately for his reputation as a disinterested scholar, he lived on into a world in which another major type of connoisseur arose. By the later twentieth century, with art history a well-established academic discipline and with works of art now mostly in museums, connoisseurs have become university-trained curators. The present curatorial type of connoisseur displays the traditional concerns of his forerunners, but he does so only for the institution by which he is employed and without personal monetary gain beyond a fixed salary.[54]

The attitude of Berenson's predecessors toward his sort of occupation was unequivocal. Jonathan Richardson, a distinguished eighteenth-century connoisseur, wrote that "understanding in a science . . . is the possessor's property, which every man sells at as good a rate as he can for value received. . . . Why connoisseurs should be expected to distinguish themselves by their generosity, or prodigality is unaccountable."[55] The reason is, of course, that works of art have a significance transcending, but not inseparable from, their commercial value. Berenson, less secure in his role than Richardson, has accordingly been described as living in "perpetual fear of discredit; his livelihood depended upon the maintenance of a delicate balance between his roles of critic and connoisseur of repute and that of a profitable intermediary."[56]

A more debatable issue than his scruples is whether Berenson's involvement with the trade affected his judgments of works of art, and, if so, how? Like other connoisseurs, Berenson provided certificates of authenticity for paintings that crossed the Atlantic. His expert opinions took the form of an artist's name inscribed on the back of a photograph or as a letter expanding on his views. This now discredited practice obviously lent itself to dishonesty, and Berenson unquestionably overpraised pictures in whose acquisition he had a stake.[57] Yet we need to see his effusions in the perspective of his training as a connois-

25

seur. Following his mentor, Morelli, the young Berenson was an iconoclast. In reattributing pictures, however, he actually underestimated many of them, as he later realized. Giorgione's *Judith* in the Hermitage Museum, for instance, he doubted was anything more than a copy of a lost original.[58] Berenson once said too that Bellini's great *Feast of the Gods* was largely by a minor follower named Basaiti. Some time later, when the work was offered for sale, he recommended it, without exaggeration in this case, as "one of the greatest imaginative conceptions" of the Renaissance.[59]

At the time early Italian pictures began to enter American collections, the pendulum of attribution was swinging, as it was bound to do, from the narrow and exclusive Morellian view to a broader, more expansionist approach to the problem of authorship. Though it can hardly be coincidental that so many favorable opinions were given, in Berenson's case, at least, there is no evidence to suggest that he ever made an attribution he did not genuinely believe at the time it was made. "Mature interest," he explained, "leads one at least as much to the mind of the artist as to his hand. An artistic personality includes not only all that the artist did in his best moments, but all that his mind conceived in the terms of his art, in whatever shape it has been recorded, no matter how inadequate, nor how unsatisfactory."[60] To prevent any misunderstanding about why he changed his mind, Berenson ought to have qualified his generous reattributions with the statement just quoted.

For some thirty years Berenson worked for the dealer whom he is said to have called the "king of the jungle"—Sir Joseph Duveen [53, illus.]. The most flamboyant art dealer of the century, Duveen (1869-1939) captured the confidence of the immensely rich American collectors who

competed for old masters.[61] He persuaded his clients, moreover, that the soundness of their investment depended, at least in the Italian field, upon Berenson's stamp of approval. In exchange for authenticating pictures, Berenson got a commission on sales and, after the Benson collection was purchased by Duveen in 1927, an annual retainer. It is clear from the business letters exchanged that the terms of their profit-sharing agreement were not fixed. They were subject to negotiation, as when Berenson wrote that "you, of course, are asking my opinion for the firm & on the usual terms, ten per cent of what you pay out for each item. Moreover, you are going to keep all that I tell you to your-

self & not pass it on to others. I cannot afford to give my opinion gratis." He added of another picture that had been obtained for "next to nothing, I expect to have a good share of the profit if you sell it at its proper value."[62]

Because Berenson and Duveen neither liked nor trusted each other, they communicated through Duveen's right-hand man at the Paris branch, Edward Fowles (1885-1971). Fowles' recently published recollections of Berenson, though not unsympathetic to him, are incomplete.[63] It is, rather, the almost weekly correspondence with Fowles that plainly reveals the nature of Berenson's dealings with the firm. Beneath the pleasantries lay serious professional disagreements. The con-

53. Sir Joseph Duveen. National Portrait Gallery, Smithsonian Institution

tainly by Ercole Roberti as certainly as attributions can be. What you ask me to do I had rather not call by its right name. This much I can say that for 40 years I have resisted such sollicitations. I hope to resist them to the end of the chapter." This he then deleted, adding more simply: "The profiles of Giov. Bentiv. & his wife are not by Cossa. What can I do about it?" Fowles persisted with a telegram [57, illus.] on April 9: "As client believes Cossa because all German experts give this attribution and as he not interested if by another master should we sell as Cossa would you flatly contradict?" Two days later Berenson

54. Ercole Roberti, *Giovanni II Bentivoglio*. National Gallery of Art, Samuel H. Kress Collection 1939

55. Ercole Roberti, *Ginevra Bentivoglio*. National Gallery of Art, Samuel H. Kress Collection, 1939

flict was between Fowles' unwavering loyalty to the commercial interests of the firm, in which he had worked his way up, and Berenson's integrity as an independent scholar. The record shows that, although Berenson had reason to regret his involvement with the picture trade, he acquitted himself very well.

A revealing incident concerns the pair of profile portraits of Giovanni Bentivoglio [54, illus.] and of his wife Ginevra [55, illus.], which, as part of the Kress collection, came to the National Gallery. On March 29, 1935, Fowles wrote Berenson [56], then in Tripoli, that "we are in rather a dilemma, as [their client Baron] Thyssen seems to know the two Dreyfus pictures under the name of Cossa, and he wants Cossas. If we told him you consider them to be Ercole Roberti, he would take no further interest in them and we may lose a future good client for Italian pictures. . . . Supposing we sell these two pictures to him as

27

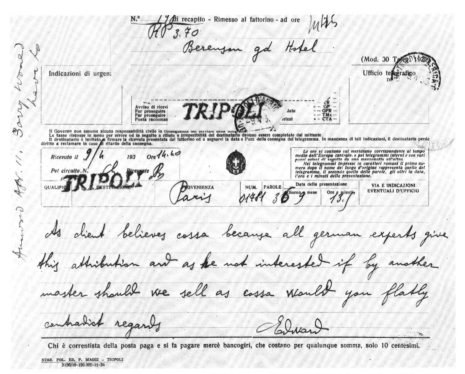

57. Telegram from Edward Fowles to Bernard Berenson, with reply along left margin, 1935. Villa I Tatti, Harvard University Center for Italian Renaissance Studies

Cossas, what will your attitude be, and what can you do to help us in the matter?"

Berenson annotated Fowles' letter, in its margin, on April 3 as follows: "The Dreyfus pictures in question are not possibly by Cossa & almost cer-

penned his reply: "Sorry, would have to."[64]

Though their interests were thus not always identical, Berenson, like Duveen, tried to monopolize his own field of expertise. The competitiveness that led him and his colleagues to rivalry may be typical of his period. But it has also dogged connoisseurship, which, for all its claims to objectivity, remains a personal pursuit. Berenson inherited from Morelli the most formidable of his adversaries, Wilhelm von Bode (1845-1929). Aside from their scholarly differences, Bode, as director of the old Kaiser Friedrich Museum in Berlin, competed with Berenson for Italian pictures.

What Roger Fry [58] wrote about early Italian painting made him appear to challenge Berenson too.[65] Nonetheless, Fry (1866-1934) assured Mary Berenson that he did not "set myself up as a connoisseur of Italian art at all in the same category as [B.B.]. I have never had the patience or the opportunity for his kind of study. I don't think, for that reason, I am bound always to agree with him; whoever would take an intelligent and appreciative interest in his work must occasionally differ. It would be too dull if one didn't." Fry added that "such differences should be tolerated and even welcomed, for it is what helps, in so far as it is intelligent, to keep the subject alive, and though that's not important, popular among cultivated people."[66] Predictably enough, friction developed between Fry and Berenson, so that, despite Mary's efforts to bring them together, they were not reconciled until shortly before Fry's death.[67] With other scholars too, like Herbert Horne (1864-1916), F. M. Perkins (1874-1955), and Roberto Longhi

60   Giorgione, *The Adoration of the Shepherds*.   National Gallery of Art, Samuel H. Kress Collection 1939

28

(1887-1970), Berenson's relations tended to follow a pattern of dispute, estrangement, and reconciliation toward the end of his life or theirs [59].

The so-called Allendale Nativity [60, illus.], now in the National Gallery, is celebrated as the cause of the rift between Berenson and his long-time employer Duveen. Berenson refused to attribute the painting to Giorgione, and Duveen tried in every way to get him to change his mind. Berenson's predicament may be imagined from Duveen's hopeful remark that "there must still be at least forty unknown Giorgiones somewhere around."[68] The picture was even brought from London to Berenson's country house so that he could examine it, but he stubbornly concluded that it was by the young Titian. Despite this attribution, the painting was acquired for the Kress collection [61, illus.], as by Giorgione. Berenson eventually listed the picture twice, as a work of collaboration: first, as by Giorgione (finished by Titian), and then as by Titian, "who completed the Virgin and the landscape probably left unfinished by Giorgione."[69] His idea that the Nativity was a work of collaboration may well be right and certainly deserves further consideration.

His days as an expert over for the most part, Berenson [62, illus.] returned to the role he had sought as a youth, that of spokesman for humanism. The minor masters were now of little interest to him. Yet the authorship of masterworks, like the Allendale Nativity, continued to be a matter of concern. He now approached the question of attribution not from the standpoint of labeling, however, but as a means of understanding the work of art.

61. Samuel H. Kress apartment, New York, with the Allendale Nativity. Samuel H. Kress Foundation

29

62. Bernard Berenson.
Villa I Tatti, Harvard University Center for Italian Renaissance Studies

Viewed in historical perspective, Berenson's connoisseurship may be seen to draw upon two main intellectual traditions. The first is the tradition of attribution, whereas the second and more recent is that of appreciation for early Italian art. The origins of modern connoisseurship lie in the Renaissance. During this period, the everyday ability to make visual distinctions began to be applied consciously and within the sphere of art.[70] Classical antiquities, prized by Renaissance collectors, formed a class of undated and unattributed art objects requiring identification. Thus the need arose in their day for the services of someone who could tell collectors what they had acquired. These services were provided not by any professional authenticator, as we might expect, but by artists, like Andrea Mantegna, of an appropriately classicizing bent.[71]

More interesting for our purposes, though, are the efforts of one Renaissance artist to differentiate painting styles of his contemporaries and predecessors. Giorgio Vasari (1511-1574), famous as the author of the *Lives of the Most Eminent Painters, Sculptors and Architects* [63, illus.], practiced what we would call "connoisseurship," in the sense of "attribution," in two roles. As a writer of artists' biographies, he needed to decide to whom he should attribute a given work of art whenever its authorship—and thus its place in his scheme—was in question. And as a collector of drawings, he wished to label them.

In both these pursuits Vasari acted as an artist sorting out the works of artists past and present. He felt justified, "since experience teaches careful painters to recognize the various styles of artists, just as a good secretary recognizes the handwriting of his colleagues, and as everyone does that of his friends and relatives."[72] His perception that an artist's style is as characteristic as his script became a commonplace in the history of connoisseurship. The difficulty was that though he could draw on his acquaintances for attributions he made in their biographies, Vasari was obliged, for earlier artists, to depend upon tradition (often unreliable) and the evidence of their works. Consequently, many of Vasari's attributions to the founders of Florentine painting were

63. Portrait of Giorgio Vasari, in *Le Vite de Più Eccellenti Pittori, . . .* National Gallery of Art

incorrect. Worse still, he was stumped by his fellow painters when, as gifted pupils, they counterfeited their masters' styles.[73]

Vasari's confusion arose from his identification of *maniera* or style with the exterior character of an artist's work. In his view, painters could only acquire, alter, or abandon their manners in a mechanical fashion. Lacking the concept of artistic personality that lies behind modern connoisseurship, what Vasari had to say about creative imagination he couched in the form of anecdotes. His schematic biographical approach to attribution was not remedied by his later editors, and Berenson wrote of a new edition of the *Lives* that it should have been undertaken by a "connoisseur . . . that is to say, one who knows the works of art intimately, subtly, and minutely."[74]

Vasari's concern with attribution also arose out of his activity as a collector. His *Libro de' Disegni* or Book of Drawings comprised several albums of studies [64] he collected, by a variety of artists, and it was meant to illustrate the development of Italian art as described in the *Lives*.[75] In the ornamental border of one splendid sheet [65, illus.] Vasari inscribed a cartouche with the name of the artist to whom he attributed the highly finished metalpoint studies of hands— "Fra Filippo" Lippi.[76] Whatever their original relationship may have been, the decorative rearrangement of the drawings as a pair shows that they were appreciated as related and beautiful specimens of an artist's style.

30

FRA FILIPPO

65. Raffaellino del Garbo, *Study of Hands and a Sleeve*. Trustees of the British Museum

66. Thomas Rowlandson. *The Connoisseurs*. Yale Center for British Art, Paul Mellon Collection

Though he seems to have admired their spontaneous character, Vasari did not systematically compare preparatory drawings with paintings to ascertain their authorship. Unlike Berenson later, he did not regard drawings as part of a creative process culminating in a work of art, and so he was not concerned with them as a means of defining artistic personalities.

The connoisseur first emerged as a distinct type in the eighteenth century; at the same time the French term was anglicized and widely adopted to mean "an expert judge in art, as well as other matters of taste."[77] Although painters continued to advise on the art of the past for as long as they knew about it, the amateur (meaning an art lover) at this time came to the fore. Yet if persons other than painters now played the part of connoisseurs, how were they competent to judge in such matters? Indeed, one self-appointed critic toward the end of the century not only questioned the expertise of the amateur but also derided him. In a

watercolor [66, illus.] Thomas Rowlandson satirized a group of connoisseurs by implying that they were voyeurs of an erotic motif, for he shows them supposedly admiring a painting of Susanna and the Elders, in which the voluptuous lady is pursued by men like themselves. Rowlandson's drawing thereby casts doubt on the claim of connoisseurship to be concerned with artistic form. His pictorial satire seems to reflect the persistent suspicion that no one but an artist can properly evaluate whatever is artistic about a work of art. The doubts have persisted, and so has the type of connoisseur so deftly caught by Rowlandson. The figure, who, aided by an eyeglass, scrutinizes the picture in the drawing may be compared, as a type, to the image we have seen of Berenson [7, illus.], peering at a portrait.[78]

Despite Rowlandson's misgivings, as early as the eighteenth century the writings of Jonathan Richardson (1665-1745) strikingly anticipated the techniques of the modern connois-

seur.[79] As an amateur dealer and collector, Richardson was well qualified to provide the gentleman of his day with a two-part instructional manual [67], consisting of "An Essay on the Whole Art of Criticism" and "An Argument in Behalf of the Science of a Connoisseur."[80] The book aimed first to show "how to judge of the goodness of a picture, of the hand of the master; and whether 'tis an original or a copy," and then to encourage the practice of connoisseurship. Richardson advocated a systematic analysis of works of art not to describe their uniqueness but to measure their "beauties" and "defects," the result of which, he felt, was characteristic of an artist. Our method of comparing unattributed works with documented or otherwise certain ones, and originals with copies, was already highly developed in Richardson's day. He even related particular works to the general idea he had formed of an artist's manner. But what distinguishes his connoisseurship —in theory at least—is his emphasis on direct observation. As Richardson put it, the connoisseur's "business is to judge from the intrinsic qualities of the thing itself."[81] He believed that if an artist's mind was reflected in the invention, his touch could be recognized even in the rendering of details, as in a hand or finger.[82] Later, Berenson would say that an artist was characteristic especially in such minor details.

Eighteenth-century connoisseurship of early Italian art centered around drawings and reached a level of refinement that would only be achieved much later for paintings of the same period. Vasari remained for connois-

68. Augustin de Saint-Aubin (after Cochin), *Pierre-Jean Mariette*, 1765. The Metropolitan Museum of Art, Harris Brisbane Dick Fund, 1917

seurs like the Parisian Pierre-Jean Mariette [68, illus.] the chief source of information about the early Italian masters and their works. Mariette (1694-1774) went so far as to seek out drawings owned by Vasari, and his characteristic blue mount may be recognized on the sheets of studies from Vasari's *Libro* [64, 65] that we have already encountered. Keenly responsive to the quality of drawings, Mariette was also accurate about their attribution—within the limits of his knowl-

edge. He based his judgments on Vasari's and on the resemblance the drawings bore to the painting styles of the great masters. This limited method lends his connoisseurship a neatness lacking in that of Berenson, who was obliged to account for many rediscovered minor talents. [83]

69. Giorgione (?), *Cupid Bending a Bow.* The Metropolitan Museum of Art, Rogers Fund, 1911

An example of Mariette's discriminating connoisseurship is provided by a red chalk drawing [69, illus.] he once owned, now in the Metropolitan Museum. It depicts Cupid bending a bow. Mariette's attribution of the drawing to Giorgione has been supported by modern art-historical research, which points to Vasari's mention of a Cupid from Giorgione's lost mural decoration of the Fondaco de' Tedeschi in Venice. It may well be that Mariette himself connected his drawing with Vasari's comment. Note the way he set the original rectangular sheet into another one, on which is drawn a semicircular niche, suggesting that Mariette associated the foreshortened figure with a wall decoration. [84]

Whether or not Mariette was cor-

rect in attributing this drawing to Giorgione, on the basis of a hint in Vasari, he was surely right in deducing from its fine quality that it was by a major Venetian master. An amateur dealer, as well as collector, Mariette, in fact, united both of the traditional concerns of the connoisseur: the perception of quality and the recognition of individual styles among artists.

Though methodical connoisseurship thus flourished in the eighteenth century, it was limited, where early Italian art was concerned, to drawings. Mariette and his contemporaries preferred paintings by such established High Renaissance and baroque masters as Raphael and the Carracci. But between the time of Mariette and Berenson, radical changes in historical perception and taste brought the Italian

70. Larkin Goldsmith Mead, *James Jackson Jarves.* Yale University Art Gallery, Gift of Mrs. Walter Raleigh Kerr

primitives to light. If Berenson's career represents the last phase of this rediscovery, the pioneer collector of Italian primitives in America was James Jackson Jarves (1818-1888). Jarves [70, illus.] brought together a well-known group of paintings that, having aroused little interest in Boston and New York, came into the possession of Yale University in 1871.[85] The collection did not consist of masterpieces, Jarves admit-

32

71. Plate from *Art Studies. The "Old Masters" of Italy. Painting.* Marquand Library, Princeton University

72. Fiorenzo di Lorenzo, *St. Jerome.* Yale University Art Gallery, University Purchase from James Jackson Jarves

ted, but of "characteristic specimens," ranging over three centuries and intended, like earlier European collections, to illustrate the progress of Italian art. Half-apologizing for his pictures, whose aesthetic significance

he failed to grasp, Jarves treated them as companions to *Art Studies* [71, illus.], his history of Italian painting published in 1861. Accordingly, the book includes reproductions of Jarves paintings, including one of a *Penitent St. Jerome* [72, illus.] he called "Fra Filippo Lippi."

Though his moralistic ideas about art are derivative, the author of *Art Studies* reveals an experienced collector's concern with questions of authenticity and condition.[86] Jarves offered exemplary advice for the prospective connoisseur, as had Richardson, but like so many reformers, he failed to practice what he preached. Though he called for careful scrutiny of a work of art in attributing it, he was governed more by the impression it made on him than he was by any probing formal analysis. In the case of the *St. Jerome* illustrated in *Art Studies* and given today to Fiorenzo di Lorenzo, Jarves handily found a solution for the attribution of the panel by turning, as had so many other connoisseurs, to Vasari's *Lives*. There he read about a painting of that saint by Filippo Lippi that belonged to the Medici, and so, without any visual evidence, Jarves claimed that his was this version of the theme.[87]

It is his hopeful attributions to Lippi, Giotto, Masaccio, Leonardo, and other great masters, and not only American cultural backwardness, that explain why Jarves was unable to dispose satisfactorily of his pictures. The skepticism about his attributions was warranted, as they were historically rather than visually prompted. Yet there can be no doubt that he honestly regarded his collection as a comprehensive survey. And no survey would have been complete without a Fra Filippo. His motivation aside, however, the plight of the Jarves collection indicates that after the mid-century a new stage had been reached in the connoisseurship of the recently discov-

ered primitives. The practice of arbitrarily attaching names to pictures was becoming discredited. Yet if a new method was needed, Jarves himself never practiced it. Instead he went on to gather a second group of paintings for other wealthier American collectors. He died in Italy in 1888, the very year Berenson came there, as if to take up where his predecessor had left off.

Like antiquities in the Renaissance, early Italian paintings offered evidence to the nineteenth century of a vast uncharted tract of human creativity. As long as the interest in these works remained antiquarian, however, there was no compelling reason to document them, except for the sake of historical accuracy. More likely it was the growing appreciation for the primitives on the part of collectors and their corresponding rise in value that gave a whole new impetus to connoisseurship. Had Jarves been able to demonstrate that his *St. Jerome* was, in fact, the Lippi owned by the Medici, and not, as it turned out, by a minor Umbrian artist, it would have been prized much more highly. What was needed, then, was a reliable way of making attributions.

The systematic study of Italian art was first undertaken by Joseph Archer Crowe (1825-1896) and Giovanni Battista Cavalcaselle (1820-1897), the joint authors of *A New History of Painting in Italy*.[88] It was they who finally took the painstaking, direct approach to works of art long endorsed in the literature, and in so doing they contributed much to our knowledge of Italian painting. But, Berenson said, they lacked the method that was provided by Giovanni Morelli (1816-1891). Mary Berenson claimed that it was Morelli [73, illus.] who turned her husband into a connoisseur. Berenson seems to have first met Morelli, whom he may already have read at Harvard, in January 1890. Their meeting did not lead to friendship,

33

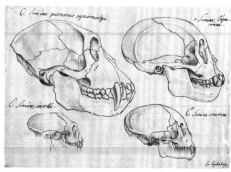

75. Giovanni Morelli, *Sheet of Drawings of Four Monkeys' Skulls.*

with Cavalcaselle in 1861 includes a sketch of Piero della Francesca's fresco of Sigismondo Malatesta in Rimini, with comments about the composition and the color of the costumes.

What really distinguished Morelli as a connoisseur, however, was his background in the study of medicine. Trained in Munich as a doctor, his specialty was comparative anatomy. This particular turn of mind is shown

73. Franz von Lenbach, *Giovanni Morelli,* 1886, Accademia Carrara di Belle Arti, Bergamo

however, as Morelli died the following year.[89]

Morelli began his career as a connoisseur—he was also a patriot and politician—with a series of polemical articles appearing in 1874-1876, in which he disconcertingly reattributed early Italian paintings in Roman galleries.   The articles were followed by a book on the galleries of Munich, Dresden, and Berlin. Definitive editions appeared in 1891-1893, and English and Italian translations quickly

34

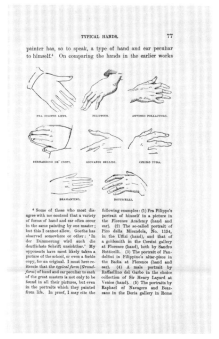

76. Johann Baptist von Spix, *Cephalogenesis,* . . . National Library of Medicine, Bethesda

77. Page from *Italian Painters. Critical Studies of Their Works.* . . . Fine Arts Library, Harvard University

74. Page from Morelli's *Notebook of a Journey to the Marches with Cavalcaselle*

followed. These works were supposed to have been written in Russian by one "Ivan Lermolieff," an anagram of Morelli's name, and translated into German by "Johannes Schwarze," a Germanization of it. In imaginary dialogues meant to mystify and confound his adversaries, Morelli assumed the identity of a Russian seeking instruction in the fine arts.[90]

Like Cavalcaselle, Morelli—in the beginning at least—relied on his own drawings of works he had seen. A hitherto unknown notebook [74, illus.] he made of a journey to the Marches

in an unpublished sheet of drawings of four monkeys' skulls [75, illus.] that Morelli made as a student. More interesting even than the subject of the drawings is their origin. They have all been accurately copied from J. B. Spix's manual of comparative anatomy entitled *Cephalogenesis* [76, illus.] of 1815. Morelli's anatomical copies after Spix's manual illuminate his later method of copying and thereby recording how painters rendered human anatomical details. Plates delineating hands [77, illus.] and ears [78], from one of Morelli's books, indicate how he adapted his medical training to the study of art. He sought thereby to give his study a scientific basis.

Though Morelli believed that the whole of a work of art was characteristic of an artist, the revolutionary method of attribution he devised emphasized the isolation and careful one-to-one comparison of the forms of hands and ears, among other motifs, which were peculiar to an artist. Such traits, which had passed unperceived by the critics, Morelli presumed would also be overlooked by a copyist or imitator. Morphological comparisons thus seemed to him to offer objective criteria for authorship; for "so long as we trust only to the general impression for identifying a work of art," Morelli warned, "instead of seeking the surer testimony of the forms peculiar to each great master with which observation and experience have made us familiar, we shall continue in the same atmosphere of doubt and uncertainty, and the foundations of the history of art will be built as heretofore on shifting sands." He was convinced that "it is absolutely necessary for a man to be a connoisseur before he can become an art historian, and to lay the foundations of his history in the gallery and not in the library."[91]

Morelli's greatest discovery concerned a mislabeled picture in the Dresden Gallery that he identified as Giorgione's *Sleeping Venus*. Still more important than any single reattribution, however, was his reconstruction of the early work of Correggio. One of eight previously unrecognized pictures he added to the artist's oeuvre, the little *Mystic Marriage of St. Catherine* [79, illus.] is now in the National Gallery. Morelli observed of the painting that the "hands, with the broad metacarpus, resemble those of Lorenzo Costa, but the expression and movement of St. Francis are wholly Correggesque, and such as we find in his later works. The form and decoration

of the throne bear much resemblance to the throne in the altarpiece with St. Francis in the Dresden Gallery," Correggio's first documented work.[92]

Examining what Morelli said about the painting, we are led to question whether he reached his results from science, as he claimed. Admittedly, he cited an anatomical form—the hand—to demonstrate a point he made elsewhere: that Correggio's style was Ferrarese in origin (Costa). And to prove that the picture was by Correggio he compared another minor, architectural detail to one in a work certainly by the artist. Nonetheless, we may suspect that the real basis for Morelli's attribution was the more basic features of the painting, such as the "expression and movement" of a figure that he found "wholly Correggesque."[93] In any case, Morelli's approach has, partly due to Berenson, been broadened in the twentieth century, so that not only morphological idiosyncrasies but more

79. Correggio,
*The Mystic Marriage of St. Catherine.*
National Gallery of Art,
Samuel H. Kress Collection 1939

essential factors of style are taken into account in making attributions. And if objective means of authentication are still sought, the lasting importance of Morelli's contribution—and the reason he was so often right—is that by focusing on details, even if too exclusively, he was led to look carefully at paintings. We take this way of regarding art for granted, but in Morelli's day, for Berenson too, it was new.

To Morelli's means of classification, Berenson added a quality of mind derived from yet another tradition, that of late nineteenth-century aestheticism, specifically as it relates to the Italian primitives. This tradition, however, was first preceded by approaches that were by no means aesthetic. The identifiable beginnings of a pre-aesthetic response to early Italian art date from just before and during the Napoleonic era, when members of the French colony in Rome took up what had previously been an erudite

35

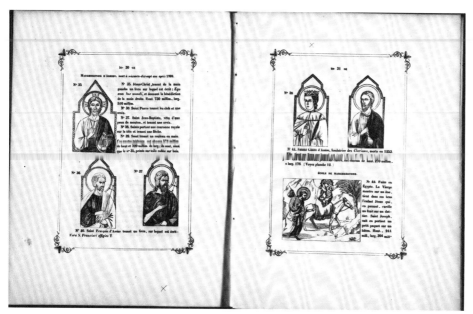

80. Pages from *Peintres Primitifs*.
Villa I Tatti, Harvard University Center for Italian Renaissance Studies

writer, Alexis Francois Rio (1798-1874), gave no impetus to connoisseurship, his writings about the early Italian masters, translated as *The Poetry of Christian Art,* did arouse widespread sympathy for their works.[99] Rio's Protestant counterpart was the mid-Victorian moralist Lord Lindsay (1812-1880), who wrote *Sketches of the History of Christian Art* in 1847.[100] But it was Mrs. Anna Brownell Jameson [82, illus.] who was the most widely

82. Portrait of Anna Brownell Jameson in *Sacred and Legendary Art*.
Library of Congress

36

local interest in past culture.[94] Chief among these pioneers was Seroux d'Agincourt (1730-1814), whose *Histoire de l'Art par les Monumens* (1811-1820) provided the first survey, amply illustrated, of medieval, as well as Renaissance art. More than a century before Berenson, d'Agincourt came to Italy, where he employed copyists to record the works he found in churches and collections. Unlike Berenson, however, his interest in Raphael's forerunners was essentially historical, not aesthetic.

The broad scope of d'Agincourt's book is reflected in the collection of early Italian paintings formed by a disciple named Artaud de Montor (1772-1849).[95] By the early nineteenth century, de Montor had gathered—easily and cheaply, we may suppose—a representative group of no fewer than one hundred and fifty pictures. We cannot assume, however, that de Montor recognized any artistic merit in these paintings, only that he meant by acquiring them to recover a small but significant part of the past. Some years later he issued a catalogue [80,

illus.] of his holdings and two National Gallery paintings we find are among them. One is the profile portrait of a young man that Berenson later called the "Artaud de Montor Masaccio."[96] The other consists of three panels [81] from a polyptych, depicting a hieratic half-length Christ flanked by saints. Not much of a connoisseur, de Montor catalogued the picture as by the thirteenth-century master Margaritone from Arezzo. Berenson, who made a study of it, more plausibly suggested the Florentine, Cimabue. Specialized research has since shown that the painting is by an anonymous Cimabue follower.[97]

A different pre-aesthetic approach to the primitives was taken by painters, such as the Nazarenes, and by writers who admired what they called "Christian art."[98] Their advocacy focused on different qualities as the source of value in paintings. It marks a new stage in the reevaluation of a style whose artless simplicity was now found spiritually rewarding and not only of antiquarian interest.

Although the pious French Catholic

read English writer on art during the nineteenth century—to judge from the many editions of her books. In illustrated volumes, collected under the title *Sacred and Legendary Art,* Mrs. Jameson chided connoisseurs for their preoccupation with the established masters and their indifference to the value of subject matter, which she elucidated from early Christian times onward, emphasizing the primitives. The copy exhibited of her *Legends of the Madonna as Represented in the Fine Arts* [83, illus.] reproduces a Peruginesque *Annunciation* [84]. Significantly, the illustration omits the grotesques which appear below in the painting and which, though integral to it, might otherwise have detracted from her discussion of the event portrayed. Mrs. Jameson was no connoisseur, but her descriptions came

83. Plate from *Legends of the Madonna as Represented in the Fine Arts*. National Gallery of Art

from and prompted a careful examination of the subject of a painting. The kind of iconographical variations she noted correspond to the idiosyncrasies of form that captured the attention of Morelli and Berenson. Though inspired by Rio, Mrs. Jameson's contribution goes beyond his moralistic approach because she evolved what amounted to a new way of scrutinizing works of art.[101] We have seen that an antiquarian interest first readmitted the precursors of the preferred masters into the history of art. Then, in moralizing about artists like Angelico and Perugino, Mrs. Jameson gave another reason to admire their work.

An aesthetic response to the early painters was beginning to emerge, however impure. Its equivocal spokesman was John Ruskin (1819-1900), the greatest and most influential art critic of his time. Ruskin [85, illus.] was much indebted to Rio and Lindsay, whose religious bias he nevertheless transcended in critical passages of great beauty and insight.[102] He placed value not only on the religious message of a work of art but also on its form. In *Modern Painters* and

other essays, Ruskin wrote sympathetically about the "primitives," the term that now began to be used in praise of a pre-Renaissance painter or picture.[103]

By the time Berenson came to Oxford in 1888, madness had forced Ruskin from the lecture podium, and Berenson afterwards claimed to have read the author little or not at all.[104] Perhaps he agreed with his wife, who wrote that it is "easy to say that [Ruskin] is a great prose writer who happened to treat of art; an eloquent moralist who drew sermons from pictures and buildings; a brilliant but hopelessly contradictory thinker who astonishes by flashes of insight and irritates by confusion and wilfulness; but it would be foolish not to acknowledge in him a sensitiveness to what is beautiful in art, unprecedented in a writer and almost miraculous in a moralist."[105] His high-mindedness aside, Ruskin's intensity of vision of art and nature permeates his writings and can hardly have failed to impress Berenson.

Berenson's attitude toward early Italian painting may not come from

Ruskin, then, but it certainly owes much to the pre-Raphaelite Brotherhood. Ruskin at first believed that early Italian painting had actually been reborn in the work of the group, first formed by Rossetti, Millais, and Holman Hunt in 1848. These young men claimed to have discovered their sense of purpose while turning the pages of Carlo Lasinio's book of engravings after frescoes by early Italian artists in the Campo Santo at Pisa.[106] Yet at least in their formative years, the Brotherhood never went to Italy to seek what was supposed to be their source of inspiration. It was the second-generation pre-Raphaelite Edward Burne-Jones (1833-1898), who, deeply involved with Italian art, made no fewer than four trips there between 1859 and 1873.[107] During these he made pencil and watercolor copies of works he admired, pre-photographic records that served him later as sources for his own designs. Dating from the artist's first visit, one sheet of copies from an album [86, illus.] fea-

37

85. John Ruskin, *Self-Portrait with Blue Neckcloth*. The Pierpont Morgan Library, Gift of the Fellows

86. Sir Edward Burne-Jones, *Page from an Album of Copies*. Fitzwilliam Museum, Cambridge

88. *Charles Eliot Norton*, probably 1880s. Harvard University Archives

89. William Rothenstein, *Portrait of Walter Pater*. Library of Congress

tures details, we may note, from pictures in the Uffizi gallery: a youth's head and the Christ Child from two of Botticelli's Madonnas may be identified more easily than some flowers from a crimson robe in the *Birth of Venus*. The other sheet [87] includes figures from Giotto's frescoes in the church of Santa Croce in Florence and from Carpaccio's St. Ursula series in Venice.[108] Just as Vasari imposed his own taste on the artists' drawings he rearranged in his albums, so Burne-Jones chose to copy those motifs embodying his image of a past that existed only in imagination. Having aptly compared Burne-Jones to Mantegna in an early essay, Berenson never lost his liking for the artist's "combination of Mantegna's contours with Fra Filippo's wistfulness . . . Indeed," he admitted, "I may be his last admirer."[109]

However much he may have owed to Burne-Jones in the way he looked at Italian art, Berenson did not share the views of Charles Eliot Norton [88, illus.], who was his teacher and a friend of Burne-Jones. Jarves, who dedicated *Art Studies* to Norton (1828-1908), introduced him to Ruskin, who deeply influenced Norton's life and work.[110]

After traveling to Italy in search of an idealized medieval past, Norton returned to America to become the first professor of fine arts at Harvard. There he preached on the art and architecture of the age of Dante, about whom he was an authority. Though as a student Berenson majored in literature, he attended Norton's lectures and made his acquaintance. One day he is said to have brought Norton a book he had been reading, Walter Pater's *Studies in the History of the Renaissance,* in which the author urged an aesthetic view of life and art on his young readers. Norton returned the book, saying that it was only fit to be read in the bathroom.[111] Complaining afterwards that Norton's interest in art was only "historical and illustrative," like that of Jarves and of Mrs. Jameson, Berenson resented his teacher's lack of sympathy.[112]

To Norton's ethical approach Berenson opposed an aesthetic derived from his reading of Pater [89, illus.], who, along with Morelli, had the greatest

influence in shaping his attitude toward connoisseurship. Thus, when the youthful aspirant to culture went to Oxford in 1888, he sought out Pater, requesting permission to attend his class. Berenson was refused, and although he treasured Pater's reply [90], he never became a direct disciple, as did his friend Oscar Wilde. The *Renaissance* was, nevertheless, so important for Berenson that it even inspired him, with Pater's other writings, to make of his life a work of art.[113]

Through the contemplation of past art, Pater sought an ideal form of existence for the present. Thus, in the famous passage on *Mona Lisa*, the picture becomes a symbol, not only of Leonardo's imagination but of the whole magnetic spirit of the Renaissance. On the other hand, the essay on the school of Giorgione, added to the third edition of the *Renaissance* [91], contains the equally famous phrase "all art aspires to the condition of music." Such an emphasis on sensuous form may have seemed to Berenson to justify

38

detaching a work of art from history. In any case, he made an art-for-art's sake reading of Pater the basis for his own aesthetic. For instance, according to Pater, it was the mood of world-weariness and melancholy in Botticelli's works—he does not mention any specific quality of form—that appealed to the modern generation. By the 1880s, we gather from a *Punch* cartoon [92, illus.], veneration for Botticelli had become the mark of an aesthetic sensibility. Berenson, on the other hand, while acknowledging that his love for Botticelli came from Pater, praised the artist for his linear grace, not his sentiment.[114]

Attribution and appreciation are often said to be antithetical in Berenson's work. He himself seemed to imply such an inner conflict when, speaking of Raphael's *Sistine Madonna* in the Dresden Gallery, he related, not without irony, how he and a fellow student "stopped just for a minute or two before this masterpiece of all schools, and then we went to work."[115] Yet Berenson's sensibility served him well as a connoisseur. What he shared with Pater was chiefly a concern with the effect a work of art has on the viewer in the moment of perception. Like an artist copying a picture, he sustained contact with a work of art so that it made a deep impression his visual memory might retain. To Pater's heightened awareness, then, Berenson added Morelli's detachment, and the process by which he claimed to enter into the spirit of a work of art became, in practice, a careful scrutiny of it. Berenson's aestheticism, the delight he felt in works of art, did not allow for any narrow preoccupation with authorship, the trap into which Morelli had fallen. At the same time his need to bring order to the study of Italian painting kept him from being merely a dilettante.

Just how deeply Berenson was involved in the movement of which Pa-

**NINCOMPOOPIANA.**

*(A Test.)*

*The Squire.* "I BELIEVE IT'S A BOTTICELLI."
*Prigsby.* "OH, NO! PARDON ME! IT IS *NOT* A BOTTICELLI. BEFORE A BOTTICELLI I AM MUTE!" 
[*The Squire wishes it was.*

92. *"Nincompoopiana," from "Punch's Almanack" for 1881* (December 13, 1880). National Gallery of Art

93. Giovanni Girolamo Savoldo, *Portrait of a Knight*.
National Gallery of Art, Samuel H. Kress Collection

95. Bernard Berenson, 1891.
Villa I Tatti, Harvard University Center for Italian
Renaissance Studies

40

ter's *Renaissance* was the creed is shown by his remarks, worth quoting at length, about a *Young Knight* [93, illus.] by Girolamo Savoldo, now in the National Gallery. Coming upon the portrait in the Liechtenstein Collection in Vienna, Berenson wrote in his meticulous early hand to Mary on October 23, 1890 [94], that he

> did nothing for two hours but look at it. So absorbed in a picture I have not been in a long time. Gaston de Foix sits in a chair draped in a mustard colored cloth. He wears a breastplate over a deep crimson tunic. He holds a broken staff in his hand, to signify an early death, of course. . . . His face is turned slightly to the right. The eyes are large, soft, and indescribably beautiful; the nose straight, the mouth firm and sweet. A severer and more lovable face I never have seen. . . . If Braun has photographed it, it shall hang in my study, if ever I

have one. Who was Gaston I hardly know. . . . To be very beautiful, and to die very young, what greater distinction can there be? . . . I dare say you will think me—no, not you, but most people would think me, sentimental and namby-pamby. But *beauty is supreme,* and its greatest manifestation is in the perfect ephebe, so rare a creature that one can count them on the fingers of one hand. Gaston de Foix certainly was one.[116]

This passage is more than a perfectly Paterean reading of a Renaissance portrait which Berenson fancifully called Gaston de Foix. Mary described the young Bernard as a "beautiful and mysterious youth," and if we compare Savoldo's portrait with a photograph of Berenson [95, illus.], dating from this time, his interpretation of the painting comes to seem highly personal, even narcissistic. Though Berenson's account may tell us more about himself

than it does about this picture, his pointed descriptions are generally perceptive in what they reveal about works of art. He simply looked more carefully than Pater did.

A year or so after he first came to Italy in 1888, Berenson had an experience that was decisive for his career as a connoisseur. Sitting outside a café in the town of Bergamo, he and a friend resolved to devote their lives to connoisseurship. "We shall give ourselves up to learning to distinguish between the authentic works of an Italian painter of the fifteenth or sixteenth century, and those commonly ascribed to him. Here at Bergamo, and in all the fragrant and romantic valleys that branch out northward, we must not stop till we are sure that every Lotto is a Lotto, every Cariani a Cariani, every Previtali a Previtali. . . ."[117]

Connoisseurship was, accordingly, the theme of Berenson's first major essay on art, an unfinished fragment begun around 1894 and published as "Rudiments of Connoisseurship" [96] in 1902. In the essay Berenson claimed that the basis for connoisseurship must be the work of art itself, not documents or tradition, which serve merely to confirm an attribution made from style. Having assimilated the Morellian method of saying who painted what picture, Berenson went on to offer a logic for it. If such forms as the ear and hand were clues left unwittingly by the artist, they were significant, he decided, only in so far as they were not vehicles of expression, did not attract attention, were outside fashion, and could be unconsciously repeated. In this way Berenson's dislike for emotion in art (he preferred Piero della Francesca over Leonardo) led him, as a beginning

connoisseur, to relate the minor details on which he relied to the expressive structure of the work as a whole.

We may justly regard this method of connoisseurship of details as part of a characteristic mid-to-late nineteenth-century way of seeing works of art. As a method of attribution, however, it was inadequate and misleading. For congruence of details, the essence of the Morellian system, is necessary but not sufficient to make an attribution. A contemporary novelist, like Henry James, could have cautioned the young Berenson, with whom he was, in fact, acquainted, that it is the telling detail that counts. To be meaningful, the detail that the novelist invents and the connoisseur selects for comparison must be treated as integral to the whole conception of the artist. It is the total structure of a work of art that is characteristic.

Berenson limited himself in the essay of 1894 to the "more or less measurable elements in pictures with which the science of connoisseurship must reckon." Quality was more difficult to demonstrate. Berenson's subsequent concern with quality marks a significant advance over the method of classification devised by Morelli.[118] Here we must recall that Morelli was nearly sixty years old when he published his studies in connoisseurship. Berenson emerged upon the scene as a connoisseur at the age of thirty, with more than sixty productive years ahead. He thus had ample opportunity to discover for himself whether Morelli's views were infallible or not.

At first he believed that if the method was right, Morelli must be right; soon enough, however, the evidence of his own eyes forced Berenson to reject certain of the master's attributions and to doubt the efficacy and legitimacy of his method. Berenson grasped that connoisseurship can never be an exact science but must depend upon the intuitive and analytical capacities of an individual.

Though Berenson adopted Morelli's method, his concern with quality links him to earlier connoisseurs, like Mariette. Quality, moreover, led beyond attribution to the more difficult yet rewarding task of defining artistic personalities.[119] Berenson came to believe that if great artists differ in detail from one work to another, they maintain a more or less consistent level and type of quality. "Level" of quality simply means imitative skill and refinement. "Type" of quality is presumably what we mean by "structure." This notion seems to conjoin the two main traditions in which Berenson was working. For Pater the work of art stood for the artist's mind, whereas for Morelli it represented the product of his hand. Connoisseurship, as Berenson came increasingly to regard it, was no longer restricted to noting morphological idiosyncrasies but involved an analysis of more essential factors of style.

Though he never entirely gave it up, Berenson's dissatisfaction with the Morellian method prompted him to write further about it in a series of articles, collected as *Three Essays in Method* [97] in 1926.[120] Their stated

41

purpose was to "let students into my workshop." Berenson's previous study of medieval painting had underscored the fact that Morelli offered "no explicit method for establishing the school and date of a given work of art," when it was not a matter of attributing it to a particular master.[121] Thus, although the essays concern Renaissance painters, Berenson broadened the scope of his investigation to include costume, depicted architecture, and even iconography, as well as morphological details, in order to identify the period and place of origin of a given work. The book comprising the essays purports to show Berenson's working procedure, but it reads more like a lengthy reexamination of results reached by what must have been a more intuitive process.

From defining the nature of known artists, Berenson went on to create artistic personalities in a way that reveals much about the success and failure of modern connoisseurship. Having observed that certain paintings attributed to well-known masters were apparently the work of other, unknown artists, Berenson grouped them together under temporary designations for research and reference. In the case of the Master of San Miniato [52], for example, he chose a painting in the town of San Miniato to provide an identity for the unknown artist to whom he attributed other pictures in the same style.[122] Or else Berenson adopted a name to stand for an artist's personality, what he would have been called, we might say, had he been a painter only and not a person. This procedure worked for the so-called "Alunno di Domenico," a pupil of Domenico Ghirlandaio, whose real name, Bartolomeo di Giovanni, was discovered afterwards.[123]

The most ambitious of Berenson's creations was, of course, Amico di Sandro, that "friend of Sandro" Botticelli, most, if not all of whose paint-

100. Bernard and Mary Berenson, 1898.
    Villa I Tatti, Harvard University Center for Italian Renaissance Studies

ings turned out to be early works by Filippino Lippi.[124] No fewer than four Gallery paintings once belonged to Berenson's group, including a small panel of *Tobias and the Angel* [98]. The original name chosen for this invented master was more conventional, the "Master of the Morte di Lucrezia," referring to a work in the Pitti Gallery.[125] Berenson opted for "Amico di Sandro" presumably to lend some life to his creation, which, nevertheless, he was prepared to repudiate in the 1932 edition of the Lists. Berenson's failure to recognize these works as by the early Filippino is typical of Morellian connoisseurship. By focusing too exclusively on details, Berenson overlooked more basic similarities of style and structure that link the *Tobias* with a mature and more easily recog-

nizable production of Filippino, like the *Pieta* [99], also in the National Gallery. Berenson's invented personalities may be less convincing than those he defined for known artists. Yet it is such a concept of artistic personality that lends significance to observation about paintings. Thus it often happens that what scholars similarly observe, they interpret differently. For this reason, connoisseurship cannot be objective, as there is no practicable way to test a given concept of an artist's personality, except by means of a consensus among scholars.

Mary Berenson [100, illus.] was the first of many collaborators that also included Berenson's longtime companion, Nicky Mariano. In the pioneering days of connoisseurship, however, Mary (1864-1945) was more of a coworker than an assistant. Their correspondence, though affectionate, deals mostly with attributions. And when they traveled together, Bernard, so as not to interrupt his concentration, left Mary to perform the task of taking notes, her own and those presumably dictated by him.[126] She recalled how he "dragged me fairly fainting with fatigue from the altarpiece in one church to those in another, and confined me strictly in museums from the hour of opening to that of closing."[127] All the same, "to steal up to [paintings] in some shadowy church where the hot sunlight lay in a shining pool on the floor by the open door, to creep around the devout worshippers and to catch glimpses of what was glimmering on the altars, to whisper to each other in breathless excitement some name like 'Falconetto' or 'Giolfino' or what not, gave us a joy I cannot hope to communicate."[128]

Mary claimed to have joined Bernard in drawing up the pamphlet on the Venetian exhibition of 1895 [15, illus.], and, in fact, their annotated copy of the official catalogue at I Tatti shows that it was she who crossed out the name of Giorgione for the *Holy Family* [16, illus.] and wrote "Catena." How they worked together may be seen in two notebooks, which reveal that Bernard and Mary actually put into practice the method they had learned from reading Morelli. One [101], recording trips to Venice and the Veneto in 1891-1893, includes a sheet with Mary's rendering of the type of ear depicted by Gentile Bellini on the organ shutters of San Marco. The other hitherto unpublished notebook [102, illus.], made in north Italy in 1892-1893 and again in Mary's hand, includes comments and sketches of the sort found in Morelli's notebook [74, illus.], hers relating to the Perugino altarpiece in the church of Sant'Agostino in Cremona. Her efforts to render Perugino's characteristic type of hand

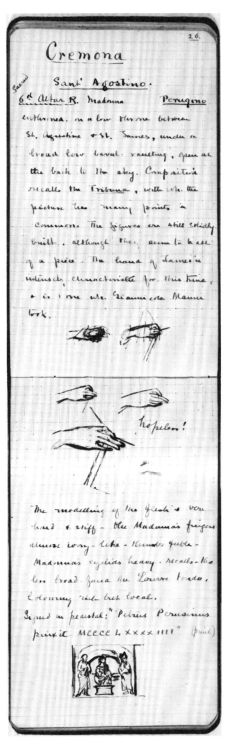

102. Bernard and Mary Berenson, pages from a *Notebook Made in North Italy.* Barbara Strachey Halpern

she finally gave up as "hopeless!"

The impression we gain of Mary Berenson in the biographies of her husband dates from the time when she had given up research to devote herself to his career and to her own family. Because she signed herself Mary Logan, the pseudonym she adopted, it is not generally recognized that it was Mary who, as a fine scholar in her own right, first contributed more than Bernard did to the literature on Italian painting. Moreover, it was Mary, not Bernard, who lectured on connoisseurship during their epochal trip to America in 1903-1904 and afterwards. Among her writings, she even reviewed Berenson's *Florentine Painters*, referring to it as "something of a surprise"![129] An ideal subject for a feminist, we might say, Mary's writings betray early signs of interest in the female role in art and literature.[130] Soon they became more specialized, as she shared Bernard's passion for connoisseurship.[131] Mary's more selective approach is suggested by her *Guide to the Italian Pictures at Hampton Court* [103] of 1894, in which she aimed to separate the wheat from the chaff. The catalogue, compiled according to Morellian principles, was undoubtedly a joint effort, but in this case, Mary got the credit. For all her application, though, Mary tired of the minor masters who occupied more and more of Berenson's attention, as he updated the Lists, and she gradually withdrew from the project.

The kind of painstaking effort that lies behind the laconic Lists may be appreciated from a comparison of two editions, the later one incorporating corrections made in Mary Berenson's hand, to the first. Appended to the four essays on the Italian painters of the Renaissance of 1894-1907 were indexes of their works [104, illus.]. The indexes were meant merely to inform the reader where to find typical works by the masters treated in the essays.

43

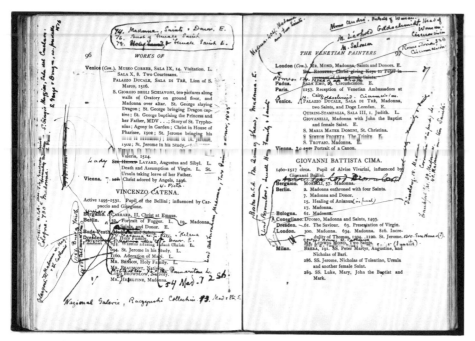

104. Pages from *The Venetian Painters of the Renaissance*.
Villa I Tatti, Harvard University Center for Italian Renaissance Studies

They were not inclusive. However, continual research and the tracing of pictures from one collection to another necessitated an edition in which all the schools were brought together: the *Italian Pictures of the Renaissance* [105] of 1932. The indexes, in other words, outgrew the essays. To be exhaustive, the new Lists of works assigned to painters by Berenson included workshop products, copies, and imitations. The changes show that Berenson conceived of attributions as hypotheses, to be advanced and confirmed or discarded. Eventually the Lists got so long that they separated again. The last, illustrated editions [106] came out shortly before and even after Berenson's death in 1959.[132]

If lists are physical traces of a process of comparison and revision, photographs are the tools of that process. It was Morelli, according to Berenson, who first made systematic use of photographs, as well as drawings, to aid him in recalling art works he had seen. Morelli's adoption of the new medium follows logically from his selection of

shapes as characteristic of an artist rather than colors and textures, which the camera failed to record adequately. Among the first generation of scholars that took to photography, Berenson in particular embraced it as the essential

44

if "uncertain instrument" of modern connoisseurship. The "patient comparison of a given work with all other works by the same master" he found to be greatly aided by photographs, which could be used to confirm or even to make attributions.[133]

Travel to study works of art was facilitated by another modern technological innovation, fast transportation in the form of the railway and automobile. Though at first he envisaged "the visiting not only of every public gallery in Europe, but of the even more numerous and frequently inaccessible private collections,"[134] and though he omitted paintings from the early Lists because he had not examined them,[135] half a century later Berenson confessed that "on the pretext of having to see certain works of art [107] and to see them where they grow, I make costly tours and give them time that in deepest conscience I suspect of being unnecessary. For the task in hand, the time could have been better spent in the library, with books and photographs. It is there, and not picnicking around, that scholarship is apt to be

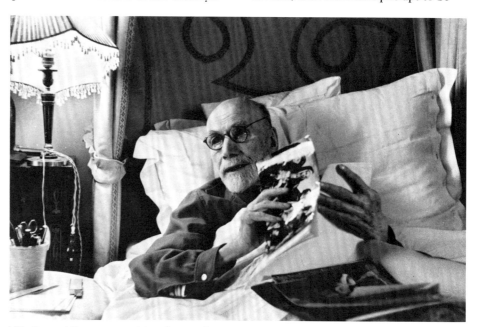

108. Bernard Berenson examining photographs, 1956.
Villa I Tatti, Harvard University Center for Italian Renaissance Studies

most creative and productive."[136] At least for the "purpose of determining when and where and by whom a given design was invented, a good reproduction," he decided, "is enough." In his daily work Berenson actually came to prefer photographs, which enabled him to prolong his capacity for study [108, illus.].[137] Berenson thus distinguished between classification, for which photographs are suitable, and enjoyment of the actual work of art, for which there is no substitute.

Other scholars, likewise concerned about the proper use of photographs in research, recommended them only as memoranda of works of art.[138] The danger they foresaw was that, unlike a hurried pencil sketch, a photograph might replace the original as an object of study. Sir Kenneth Clark has recently recounted just such an abuse of photography in connoisseurship. As a young apprentice at I Tatti, he was given the Titian folder to prepare. "At that time I had not been to the Prado," he admitted, "nor Vienna, nor even Venice. Nothing could show more clearly the hollowness of the system of art-historical studies then fashionable, and still, I believe, in certain institutions, that I should have been expected to determine from photographs alone, the authenticity of works by a supreme colorist."[139]

Nevertheless, photographs provide an indispensable way of comparing works of art too numerous and too distant geographically to be studied directly, and connoisseurs began at once to collect them, eventually forming archives that have since become available to other qualified scholars. The photographs gathered by Berenson, for instance, many of them from dealers and collectors, have been reinstalled at I Tatti [109]. Those belonging to his colleague George Martin Richter became the nucleus for the now vastly expanded holdings of the National Gallery's Center for Advanced Study in

the Visual Arts. To supply this need for large quantities of photographs, commercial archives grew up. Berenson reported on the wide-ranging campaigns undertaken in the 1890s by Anderson of Rome and the Alinari brothers of Florence, both with extensive inventories of Italian material.[140] What the amassing of photographs amounts to is that the trained memory of connoisseurs of Berenson's generation was supplemented or even substituted by a mechanical faculty of visual recall, a "democratic" process parallel to the way photography itself enabled unskilled draftsmen to create images.

"Photographs! Photographs!" Berenson exclaimed in the 1932 edition of the Lists. "In our work one can never have enough." How he used photo-

graphs to revise the Lists may be seen in relation to Andrea del Castagno's *Portrait of a Man* [110, illus.] in the National Gallery. This forceful portrait was recorded by the Berensons in the early 1890s, when it belonged to the Torrigiani family in Florence. Soon afterward they saw it again in another collection in Paris. In their entries in unpublished notebooks they attributed the picture to Castagno. They described as well the vivid color lacking in an old photograph [111] of the painting. Annotations on the back of an analogous photograph [112, illus.] from I Tatti, made at intervals of many years, give the provenance and attribution history of the picture. In the upper left Mary wrote and then crossed out the name of Botticelli to

110. Andrea del Castagno, *Portrait of a Man.*
   National Gallery of Art, Andrew W. Mellon Collection 1937

45

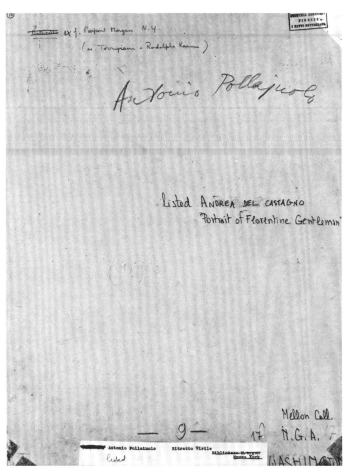

113. Raphael, *The Alba Madonna*.
National Gallery of Art, Andrew W. Mellon Collection 1937

46

112. Annotations on the reverse of a photograph of Andrea del Castagno's *Portrait of a Man*. Villa I Tatti, Harvard University Center for Italian Renaissance Studies

whom the portrait was once ascribed. Berenson, in the larger and looser handwriting of his later years, suggested, instead of Castagno, the name "Antonio Pollaiuolo." Accordingly, from a label at the bottom we learn that he gave the painting to Pollaiuolo in the 1932 and 1936 editions of the Lists. Other scholars disagreed, preferring the Castagno attribution, to which Berenson returned, and this too we gather from yet another inscription on the back of the photograph.[141] The suggestion Berenson once made of Pollaiuolo nonetheless remains worthy of consideration as an alternative to Castagno.

If modern connoisseurship depends upon photographs, their reliability as records of works of art needs to be assessed. We are concerned to know not only how the connoisseur makes his decisions but also on what basis, whether on the object itself or from photographs of it. Overcoming the hostility of museum officials, mid-nineteenth century photographers at this time began systematically to record works of art, which, because they are motionless, well suited the task.[142] By the end of the century photography had superseded metal and wood engraving and lithography as the standard method of reproducing visual images.

Before photography, masterworks of painting were engraved again and again. Two such engravings of the

*Alba Madonna* [113, illus.], made while it was in a London collection early in the nineteenth century, each make a different statement about the original. In her introduction to the catalogue of the collection, Mrs. Jameson praised the "pure and correct style" of the plates [114, illus.], drawn and engraved by F. Joubert. Much as Berenson would later use photographs, she indicated how engravings were meant to be "retranslated": "Even a slight memorandum of such a composition as . . . the Holy Family of Raphael will make it start up before the fancy in all the beauty of various tints, all the magic of chiaro-scuro."[143] This particular print (actually a lithograph after a line engraving) would prove invaluable to connoisseurs, Mrs. Jameson predicted, since the picture itself had just been acquired by the Hermitage Museum in Leningrad.

The purportedly accurate Joubert print differs from another, more elaborate folio engraving [115, illus.] by B. Desnoyers.[144] The two prints dis-

114. Plate from *Collection of Pictures of W. G. Coesvelt, Esq. of London.*
National Gallery of Art

115. A. G. Louis Boucher Desnoyers, engraving of *The Alba Madonna.*
National Gallery of Art

agree, not only in scale but also in overall tonality, as well as details of costume and setting. As Berenson said, "no engraver, however well intentioned, can help putting a great deal of himself into his reproductions."[145] Moreover, due to technical limitations of the medium—ink on paper—both prints fail to reproduce the surface characteristics—color and paint handling—of the picture. They transmit only the design. Connoisseurs before Berenson, relying on engravings, "no matter how good a general notion of a painter's various compositions they might have drawn from this source, could have next to no acquaintance with those subtlest elements of his style which distinguish him from the mere copyist or clever imitator."[146]

However inaccurate, though, engravings were preferable to the earliest photographs of paintings. The disequilibrium of color values in the old collodion negative led photographers to work from engravings after paintings. An example of such a copy of a copy of

the *Alba Madonna* appears in a monograph on Raphael [116]. The print employed may be recognized as Desnoyer's engraving. This process seems strange to us, in view of modern screened halftone reproductions, but writers on art at that time were used to dealing with reproductive engravings. Only gradually was the practice of photographing prints after paintings replaced by photographs made directly from the original works and, in book illustration, by photogravure and other photo-mechanical processes.[147]

While the artistic merits of photographs were debated, few critics thought to question their value as visual records. The very traits that tainted them as creative art—their objectivity and reproducibility—made them ideally suited as copies. Thus when orthochromatic photographs of art works first appeared in the 1880s, Berenson claimed that "leaving out the color, they are the pictures themselves on a smaller scale."[148] Yet a large format carbon print of the *Alba*

*Madonna* [117], made by Braun in the Hermitage, shows that this kind of photography of art can be misleading too.[149] The orthochromatic negative, sensitive to the cool end of the color spectrum, failed to differentiate the tonal values of the blue in the Madonna's robe and of the red in her dress; they look as if they are alike in color.

Apart from this technical deficiency, the early photograph [117] reflects a way of seeing the work reproduced characteristic of engravings. It crops the painting all around, thereby enlarging the figures at the expense of the setting Raphael provided for them. Moreover, the light-dark pattern of the photograph and its rather dry quality seem to follow the conventions of an engraving like that of Desnoyers. Another way in which this photograph misinterprets the painting has to do with the arm with which the Child supports himself on his mother's lap. This attitude, the fulcrum of what Berenson called a "triumph of centralised composition,"[150] is obscured in the photograph because the flesh tones are too dark. By contrast, the engraver [115, illus.] had the option of visually emphasizing the motif in order to convey the artist's intention.[151]

Berenson wrote Mary from Vienna on October 23, 1890, that he had bought forty-nine small photographs and three very large ones. "Don't be surprised," he added, "that two of the very large ones are of Dürer's. I got them for scientific purposes. . . . Compare the hand of the gloved visitor in Lotto's 'Madonna with St. Onophrio' of the Borghese Gallery."[152] His comment indicates that, if artists' manners could be broadly distinguished on the basis of engravings, only photographs, especially those near the scale of the original, could capture the minor details upon which Morellian connoisseurship was founded. The practice of making engraved details was not new. Juxtaposed with an overall reproduction, they served to underscore some point about the history of style.[153] A different purpose guided Braun in selecting details to photograph from the *Alba Madonna*. In one [118] showing the Madonna and Child, the hands of the little St. John have been arbitrarily removed by the photographer and the cross completed. In another [119, illus.], with the figures of the Child and St. John nearly in full scale, the Madonna's face has been omitted. These are pictorial details, complete in themselves. Such vignettes were better suited for use by the public as decoration than by art scholars for the purpose of connoisseurship.[154]

A modern museum photograph of the *Alba Madonna* [120] is more reliable than those made by Braun. It reproduces the painting entire, if at a reduced scale, and with fully rendered tonal values. A detail of the center of the painting [121, illus.] has a purely formal character. If engravings and old photographs were suited to their use in past connoisseurship, based on the artist's conception, the modern photographic detail is equally involved with modern connoisseurship. The modern photographic detail, in fact, shows the problem inherent in modern connoisseurship: a detail may be insignificant if chosen by the art historian or photographer without regard to the whole painting. A second detail of the Madonna's eye [122] is so enlarged as to be meaningless to the ordinary viewer. It too serves the purpose of scholarship.

In this century a whole range of technical photographs which report specialized information about the underlying structure of works of art have been added to photographs taken under normal conditions. One made of the *Alba Madonna* under ultraviolet radiation [123] shows some slight retouchings to the surface. An infrared photograph [124] would reveal any more

48

119. *The Alba Madonna* (detail; carbon print). Musée du Louvre

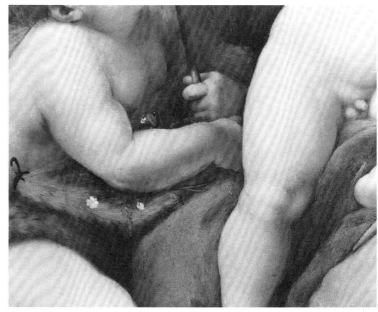

121. *The Alba Madonna* (detail). National Gallery of Art

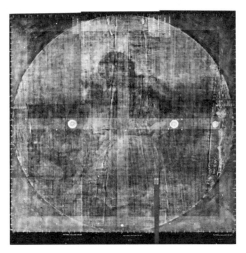

125. *The Alba Madonna* (x-radiograph photograph). National Gallery of Art

serious damage. The condition of the picture is best gauged, however, from an x-radiograph [125, illus.], permitting us to peer through the paint layers. Though Berenson never fully utilized these techniques of investigation, they enable the connoisseur to determine what remains of an artist's otherwise unseeable handiwork and, on that added basis to decide about the attribution and qualitative importance of a picture.

A noted historian of visual communication may be right that "until photography came into common use there had been no way of making pictures of objects that could serve as a basis for connoisseurship of the modern type, that is for the study of objects as particulars."[155] Nevertheless, as connoisseurs became more and more dependent upon photographs in their work, Berenson no longer believed that "photography reproduces the object as it is."[156] The kind of monochrome photographs normally used in art-historical research still miss the color, scale, and paint handling of the original. In some cases, the problem of color has been met by reasonably accurate, if sometimes flattering color transparencies [126]. Yet even the color photograph has not

reached the point where it can approximate the specific quality of a painting. Recognizing this, Berenson actually preferred black and white photographs,[157] and he returned again and again to find himself stimulated by the actual work of art. Though it has eliminated the need for lengthy descriptions of works of art, photography has, like other technological innovations, tended to remove its user from first-hand experience. In practice, as Berenson and other early connoisseurs suspected, it has all too often come to stand for the original—so much so that we speak of a photographic way of seeing works of art.

49

# AN APPRECIATION

Berenson's fine appreciation of Botticelli's *Portrait of a Youth* [illus.], now in the National Gallery, offers a final revealing insight into his working method. His remarks were prompted by the occasion he had to see the picture again, after it had been acquired by Carl Hamilton in 1921. As Mary Berenson wrote Isabella Stewart Gardner, she and Bernard were both impressed by the way Hamilton "came home last night with an adorable Botticelli under his arm, the portrait of a youth in a red cap and fur trimmed coat. It used to be in the Schickler collection, where B. B. discovered it."[158]

First [Berenson said], a few words of description, interpretation and appreciation. The portrait, a little more than half the size of life, represents a youth of the pensive, wistful, intense and abstracted type that is too self-absorbed to be free from mannerisms and too sincere to be spoiled by affectations. While the slight frame leans forward and sideways, and the heavy head would naturally tend to follow this movement, the pressure of the hand and the wide open eyes make us feel a strong effort to keep erect and awake.

Yet the face and the features, like the hand, are anything but fragile and effeminate. There is no faintest approach to the epicene in the cast of countenance and expression, the strong though sensitive nose, the firm mouth. In fact, the mask is bony and manly.

It is set off by yellowish curls and strands of hair, supple and sinuous and delightful in themselves, while serving to mass the head and shoulders in a way to avoid a silhouette too deeply indented: and this mass, which might be too broad and heavy, is lightened by an upward-sloping red cap.

As for the rest of the picture, the colour of the flesh is golden, the eyes hazel, the coat purplish brown, and the background dark.

Perhaps the most interesting thing about this portrait is the manifest competition of the hand with the face. The hand is studied just as carefully, drawn and modelled with as much intention, as the face itself. Its action reveals the automatic nervous tension of an overstrung physique that the conscious mind, controlling the expression, tries to keep in order. It thus becomes, in a sense, the most important clue to understanding the character. If you think it away, the expression, of course, remains, but what makes it comprehensible disappears. On the contrary, if by some queer accident the head were missing, we could in all essentials complete it from the contrasted movements of the chest and the hand.

This complex and rather contradictory personality is expressed in terms of art by a pattern which also follows a double rhythm. It moves downward from right to left and upward from left to right, coinciding so completely with the contrast in the character that it is impossible to think of the one except in terms of the other. I need hardly add that each detail, from the ripple of the hair, the folds of the sleeves to the curl of the fur trimming, is under the control of this pattern.

There can be no question that this portrait is Botticelli's own handiwork. The glamour it cast when I first saw it frightened me into doubts that were dispelled directly I could study the painting at my leisure. There is no one, using this formula and technique, but Sandro himself who has the sinuous line, the inevitable contours, the structural articulation, the firmness, convincingness and delicacy of modelling this work possesses, nobody else who could produce a rhythm so subtly vibrant, or could give this limpid, radiant and aetherial colouring.

True, it is more "Botticellian" than any other Botticelli in existence. He must have uttered this completest note of his own music just before he was seized by the Savonarolian madness, from which he never recovered, just at the moment when he was most peculiarly and poignantly and, if I may say so, most extravagantly himself. The isolation of this head, too, exaggerates the impression. Perhaps if we found it as an Angel in a "Magnificat" or a "Madonna with the Pomegranate," in a "Tobias" or some Allegory, the other figures, the landscape and all the accessories would prevent our attention from concentrating on what is almost uncannily characteristic of the master's style.[159]

50

Botticelli, *Portrait of a Youth.*
National Gallery of Art, Andrew W. Mellon Collection 1937

## NOTES

1 "A Madonna by Antonello da Messina," in *The Study and Criticism of Italian Art*, 3rd s. (London, 1916), 79-95 (reprinted from *Gazette des Beaux-Arts*, 1913, 189-203). About connoisseurship in general, see: Richard Offner, "Connoisseurship," *Art News, 50*, no. 1 (Mar. 1951): 24-25, 62-63; James Ackerman (with Rhys Carpenter), *Art and Archaeology* (Englewood, N.J., 1963), 203-211; W. Eugene Kleinbauer, *Modern Perspectives in Western Art History* (New York, 1971), 43-40, and Mark Roskill, *What is Art History?* (New York, 1976), 19-35.

2 Kenneth Clark, *Another Part of the Wood* (London, 1974), 138.

3 *Sketch for a Self-Portrait* (London, 1949), 132.

4 *Leonardo da Vinci. An Account of his Development as an Artist* (Cambridge, 1939), and *A Catalogue of the Drawings of Leonardo da Vinci at Windsor Castle*, 2 vols. (Cambridge, 1935). Clark has reminisced about Berenson in a sequel to the *Civilisation* series and in *The Burlington Magazine, 102*, no. 690 (Sept. 1960): 381-386. Chapters in both volumes of his autobiography deal with Berenson too. See *Another Part of the Wood*, 123-165; and *The Other Half. A Self-Portrait* (London, 1977), 103-108.

5 About Pope-Hennessy's debt to Berenson see *Essays on Italian Sculpture* (London-New York, 1968), vii, ix, and especially 199-208, "Portrait of an Art Historian," (reprinted from *The Times Literary Supplement*, Mar. 25, 1960).

6 Prof. Freedberg kindly and preceptively remarked upon his relationship to Berenson in a letter to the author dated Aug. 31, 1978.

7 *The Study and Criticism of Italian Art* (London, 1901), v.

8 For his inner conflict see the late diaries (*Sunset and Twilight* [New York, 1963], 400; and *The Bernard Berenson Treasury* [New York, 1962], 258, 272).

9 Meyer Schapiro, "Mr. Berenson's Values," in *Encounter, 16*, no. 1 (Jan. 1961): 57-65.

10 *Self-Portrait*, 35-36. About Berenson's theories see Rene Wellek, "Vernon Lee, Bernard Berenson, and Aesthetics," in *Friendship's Garland—Essays Presented to Mario Praz, 2* (Rome, 1966): 233-251.

11 *The Selected Letters of Bernard Berenson*, ed. A. R. McComb (Boston, 1964), 270 (July 6, 1952).

12 *Letters of Roger Fry*, ed. Denys Sutton (New York, 1972), no. 80.

13 *Exhibition of Venetian Art. The New Gallery, Regent Street, 1894-95.*

14 The paperbound pamphlet, printed at the expense of the organizer of the exhibition and sold there, was republished in Berenson's *Study and Criticism* (1901), 90-146.

15 *Venetian Painting Chiefly before Titian* (1895), 32-33, reprinted in *Study and Criticism* (1901), 133. The painting had already been listed as Catena's in the 1894 edition of the *Venetian Painters of the Renaissance*, 103. Berenson rejected the Giorgione attribution given to a drawing in the exhibition (*Venetian Painting*, 41), which is also exhibited here [69, illus.].

16 Letter in the Gallery's files dated Oct. 24, 1953. The picture appears as Giorgione's in *Italian Pictures of the Renaissance. Venetian School, 1* (London, 1957): 85.

17 See *Venetian Painting*, 8-9 or *Study and Criticism* (1901), 97-98.

18 See *Study and Criticism* (1901), n. 1, p. 98; *The Study and Criticism of Italian Art*, 2nd s. (London, 1902), 55-56; and *North Italian Painters of the Renaissance* (London, 1907), 255.

19 "A New 'Mantegna' for America," in *Art in America, 6*, no. 3 (Apr. 1918): 127-128; *Italian Pictures of the Renaissance* (Oxford, 1932), 328; *Italian Pictures of the Renaissance. Central Italian and North Italian Schools, 1* (London, 1968): 242.

20 The full title is: *Drawings of the Florentine Painters, Classified, Criticized, and Studied as Documents in the History and Appreciation of Tuscan Art with a Copious Catalogue Raisonné*. Later editions are: *Drawings of the Florentine Painters*, 3 vols. (Chicago, 1938); and *I Disegni dei Pittori Fiorentini*, trans. Luisa Vertova Nicolson (Milan, 1961).

21 *Three Essays in Method* (Oxford, 1927), p. 83.

22 *Lorenzo Lotto. An Essay in Constructive Art Criticism* (New York-London, 1895), 1-3, 316-318. The picture had already been recognized as an early Lotto by Morelli (*Italian Painters. Critical Studies of their Works. The Galleries of Munich and Dresden* [London, 1893], 46). It was shown at the New Gallery exhibition of 1895, no. 60 (*Venetian Painting*, 19).

23 *Sunset and Twilight*, 264. About Berenson's importance for American collectors see: Gerald Reitlinger, *The Economics of Taste* (London, 1961), 197-202. Berenson commented on the scarcity of early Italian pictures in America in "Les Peintures Italiennes de New York et de Boston," *Gazette des Beaux-Arts, 15* (1896): 195-214. Berenson's *Venetian Painting in America. The Fifteenth Century* (New York, 1916), though no mere collectors' handbook, does survey Venetian pictures that had crossed the Atlantic under his auspices. What is remarkable about the book is that such a satisfactory account of the school could be constructed out of American holdings brought together in less than two decades. More straightforward surveys are Lionello Venturi's *Italian Paintings in America*, 2nd ed. rev., 3 vols. (New York-Milan, 1933); and his "Private Collections of Italian Paintings," *Art in America, 32*, no. 4 (Oct. 1944): 168-177.

24 Letter of Oct. 5, 1890, quoted in Mary Berenson's "Unpublished Life" of her husband, chap. 2, preserved in typescript in the archive at I Tatti.

25 Letters from Berenson to Mrs. Gardner, Aug. 9, 1902 (deposited at the Gardner Museum), published in *Selected Letters*, 68-69.

26 *The American Scene* (London, 1907), 192. James added: ". . . except creation."

27 The journal was kindly brought to my attention by Prof. Myron Gilmore, who published it in part in "The Berensons and Villa I Tatti," *Proceedings of the American Philosophical Society*, *120*, no. 1 (Jan. 1976): 7-12.

28 Between 1895 and 1901 four pictures came through Berenson to the Gardner collection from J. P. Richter (1847-1937). See Philip Hendy, *European and American Paintings in the Isabella Stewart Gardner Museum* (Boston, 1974), nos. P30w9, P26e17, P26w11, and P26w8. Additional Italian paintings can be traced from the Philadelphia collection of John G. Johnson (1841-1917), for whom Berenson acted as an advisor, back to yet another Morellian, Gustavo Frizzoni (1840-1919). The correspondence between Berenson and Frizzoni is preserved in part at I Tatti, and like that with Richter, it deals largely with commerce in works of art (Nicky Mariano, *The Berenson Archive. An Inventory of Correspondence* [Florence, 1965], 36).

29 About Berenson and Mrs. Gardner, see Rollin van N. Hadley and Frances E. Preston, "Berenson and Mrs. Gardner. The Venetian Influence," *Fenway Court*, Isabella Stewart Gardner Museum [Boston], 1972, 11-17; and "Berenson and Mrs. Gardner: The Museum Years," *Fenway Court*, 1974, 5-13. About her museum see Hendy, *Gardner Museum* and *The Connoisseur*, *198*, no. 795 (May 1978).

30 About the picture, see Charles Seymour, Jr., *Early Italian Paintings in the Yale University Art Gallery* (New Haven-London, 1970), cat. no. 87, pp. 128-130. In correspondence with Jarves' biographer, Francis Steegmuller, Berenson claimed his first acquaintance with this and other Jarves paintings was through an article on the collections by William Rankin, published in *American Journal of Archaeology*, *10*, no. 2 (Apr.-June 1895). Rankin had already observed that although the "Botticelli" at first might seem the best picture Jarves owned, it was by the artist's school (p. 146). The Berensons visited the Jarves collection again on Feb. 7, 1914 (letter to Isabella Stewart Gardner of Feb. 6) and on Jan. 29, 1921 (letter of Jan. 21, 1921, to Prof. Paul Sachs [*Selected Letters*, p. 89]).

31 Letter from Mary Berenson to Isabella Stewart Gardner, Dec. 5, 1908; deposited at Fenway Court.

32 Letter from Mary Berenson to Isabella Gardner, Dec. 16, 1908; deposited at Fenway Court. The Berensons returned to the collection again in 1914 (letter to Mrs. Gardner of Jan. 28, 1914; deposited at Fenway Court).

33 About the Wideners as collectors see W. G. Constable, *Art Collecting in the United States of America* (London-New York, 1964), 115-119.

34 Joseph Widener's letter to Berenson, dated Mar. 5, 1912, is preserved at I Tatti, with the remainder of their correspondence.

For the arrangement of the collection in the Widener house see *Fortune*, *6*, no. 3 (Sept. 1932): 62-72.

35 Another Dale picture in the National Gallery owned by the Wideners is Delacroix's *Columbus* (no. 1791). Because of the good quality of this picture, the issue of change of taste is clearer than with Daumier's *Beggars*. Both these pictures were included in the catalogues of the Widener collection of 1900 and 1908, but do not appear in that of 1915.

36 Quoted in *Looking at Pictures with Bernard Berenson* (New York, 1974), 136.

37 About Hamilton's apartment, see Nicky Mariano, *Forty Years with Berenson* (New York, 1966), 36-37. Some idea of its contents may be gained from the catalogue of a *Loan Exhibition of Paintings, Furniture, and Art Objects from the Collection of Carl W. Hamilton*, Montclair Art Museum, Montclair, New Jersey, Dec. 10, 1925-Jan. 10, 1926. In addition, Mr. Charles Payne, on a visit to the National Gallery of Art, kindly provided the writer with a description of one room in the apartment (approximately 10 x 15 ft.) as it appeared around 1920. On one of the shorter walls hung Piero della Francesca's *Crucifixion*, now belonging to the Frick Collection, while on the opposite wall was Botticelli's *Portrait of a Boy*, which came to the National Gallery. On one of the larger walls over a couch was Mantegna's *Judith* [17, illus.], purchased by Joseph Widener, and opposite Bellini's *Feast of the Gods*, also acquired by Widener and also in the Gallery. On either side of Bellini's picture was a pair of panels of an Annunciation by Fra Angelico, sold to Mrs. Edsel Ford and now in the Detroit Institute of Arts.

38 About Mary's lectures see *Selected Letters*, 90-91. Mary also wrote on Bellini's *Feast of the Gods*, when it belonged to Hamilton, in *Art in America*, *9*, no. 1 (Dec. 1920): 3-5. Berenson's articles on Hamilton's pictures include the following: "A New 'Mantegna' for America"; "A Newly Discovered Cimabue," *Art in America*, *8*, no. 6 (Oct. 1920): 251-271 (reprinted in *Studies in Medieval Painting* [New Haven-London, 1930], 17-31); "A Botticelli Portrait in the Collection of Mr. Carl W. Hamilton," *Art in America*, *10*, no. 1 (Dec. 1921): 26-30; "Due Dipinti del Decimosecondo Secolo Venuti da Constantinopoli," *Dedalo*, *2*, no. 5 (Oct. 1921): 285-304 (reprinted in *Studies in Medieval Painting*, 63-74); and "Prime Opere di Allegretto Nuzi," *Bollettino d'Arte*, *1*, no. 7 (Jan. 1922): 297-308 (reprinted in *Studies in Medieval Painting*, 63-74).

39 The anecdote is repeated, somewhat varied, in Nicky Mariano, *Forty Years with Berenson*, 20, 22; S. N. Behrman, *Duveen* (Boston-Toronto, 1972), 127-128; and Edward Fowles, *Memories of Duveen Brothers* (London, 1976), 128.

40 The correspondence between Hamilton and the Berensons, preserved at I Tatti, contains numerous references to the painting. In a letter of Oct. 15, 1919, Hamilton speaks of a photograph and description of the picture, which, he anticipated, would make his apartment "radiant, and I shall become more efficient in business and richer in character." Eight days later he wrote to Mary that "I often come direct to the lovely little Pesellino . . . And it is to you and B. B. to whom I am inexpressibly grateful." On Aug. 19, 1924, he reminded Berenson of the "interesting

lovely little St. John which you and Mary gave me." Hamilton finally urged Berenson to publish his discovery that the panel, which had "attracted much attention," belonged to an altarpiece by Domenico Veneziano, in a letter of Nov. 20, 1926.

41  *Three Essays*, 25.

42  Many of the Berensons' opinions are quoted in Malcolm Vaughan, "Masterpieces in the Hamilton Collection," *Art News*, 27, no. 30 (Apr. 1929): 75-87.

43  Before they were sold, Hamilton's remaining pictures were exhibited in 1927 at Montclair, New Jersey, Toronto, and San Francisco. About two of them, a *Madonna* by Filippo Lippi and a *Crucifixion* by Piero della Francesca, see Richard Offner, *Two Masterpieces of Renaissance Painting from the Collection of Carl W. Hamilton to be Sold by Auction at Unreserved Public Sale* [May 8], Anderson Galleries (New York, 1929). About the sale see Behrman, *Duveen*, 211-212.

44  About these collectors see Constable, *Art Collecting, passim*. For the fifty or so pictures that Johnson purchased through Berenson or on his advice see Barbara Sweeny, *John G. Johnson Collection. Catalogue of Italian Paintings* (Philadelphia, 1966). Berenson himself had earlier catalogued Johnson's holdings (*Catalogue of a Collection of Paintings and some Art Objects. 1. Italian Paintings* [Philadelphia, 1913]) and corresponded with him at length about them (Mariano, *Berenson Archive*, 50). For Walters' pictures see Federico Zeri, *Italian Paintings in the Walters Art Gallery*, 2 vols. (Baltimore, 1976), esp. 1: xiii. Walters' Italianate *palazzo*, completed soon after Mrs. Gardner's in Boston, is illustrated in *Apollo, 100* (1974): 355 (special issue devoted to the collection). Perhaps the most interesting of all these Berensonian collectors was Robert Lehman, whose taste led him beyond the Italian primitives (especially the Sienese) to the modern French school, favored today. See George Szabó, *The Robert Lehman Collection*, with foreword by Joseph A. Thomas (New York, 1975), 10.

45  Letter from Rush Kress to Berenson, dated Feb. 3, 1948, deposited at I Tatti; draft of a letter to Kress from Berenson, dated Feb. 12, 1949, at I Tatti. About the Kresses as collectors see Constable, *Art Collecting*, 133-137; and John Walker, *Self-Portrait with Donors* (Boston-Toronto, 1974) 133-153.

46  Letter from Berenson to Rush Kress, dated July 29, 1947, at the Kress Foundation in New York.

47  The correspondence between Berenson and the Kresses is divided between the I Tatti Collection and the Kress Foundation in New York. For Berenson's remarks on the tondo, see "Fra Angelico, Fra Filippo and their Chronology," in his *Homeless Paintings of the Renaissance* (Bloomington-London, 1970), 198-233 (an Italian translation of the then unpublished English manuscript appeared in *Bollettino d'Arte*, 26, 3rd s. [1932]: 49-66). See also the "Postscript, 1949. The Cook Tondo Revisited," in *Homeless Paintings*, 234-243. The most recent account is in Jeffrey Ruda's "The National Gallery Tondo of the *Adoration of the Magi* and the Early Style of Filippo Lippi," *Studies in the History of Art*, National Gallery of Art, 7, (1975): 7-39.

48  About the picture see Fern Rusk Shapley, *Paintings from the Samuel H. Kress Collection. Italian Schools. XIII-XV Century* (London, 1966), 20-21.

49  The Kress collection is probably the largest collection of Italian paintings ever brought together by an individual. For an idea of its extent see: Fern Rusk Shapley, *Italian Schools. XIII-XV Century; Paintings from the Samuel H. Kress Collection. Italian Schools. XV-XVI Century* (London, 1968); *Paintings from the Samuel H. Kress Collection. Italian Schools. XVI-XVIII Century* (London, 1973).

50  Letter from David Finley to Berenson, dated Aug. 15, 1939, at I Tatti.

51  J. Carter Brown, "A Personal Reminiscence," in *Looking at Pictures*, 15-20.

52  Letter from David Finley to Berenson, dated Aug. 15, 1939, at I Tatti.

53  For Walker's moving portrayal of the aged Berenson see *Self-Portrait*, 80-101. About Berenson's collection see: Franco Russoli, *La Raccolta Berenson* (Milan, 1962); and *Great Private Collections*, ed. Douglas Cooper (New York, 1963), 60-73.

54  The emergence of the new type of connoisseur is exemplified by Richard Offner (1889-1965), who taught connoisseurship of early Italian painting at the Institute of Fine Arts at New York University. Though Prof. Offner also gave expert opinions, it was for a fixed fee, not a percentage of the price of the work sold. For his views about the practice of connoisseurship in relation to the art market see his letter to the editor in *Art in America*, Feb. 1925, 102-103; and his "Connoisseurship," *Art News, 50*, no. 1 (Mar. 1951): 24-25, 62-63.

55  Jonathan Richardson, *Two Discourses* (1719; reprint ed. 1972), 156.

56  Edward Fowles, *Duveen Brothers*, 130.

57  See, for example, the quotations from Berenson in *Duveen Pictures in Public Collections in America. A Catalogue Raisonné with Three Hundred Illustrations of Paintings by the Great Masters, which have passed through the House of Duveen* (New York, 1941).

58  *Study and Criticism* (1901), 76-77.

59  *Study and Criticism* (1901), 113-114, n. 2. Berenson's later view is quoted in a letter from the dealer Arthur Sulley to Joseph Widener of Apr. 23, 1917.

60  Preface to the 1932 edition of *Italian Pictures*, xxiii.

61  See the illustrated edition of Behrman's *Duveen* (see above, n. 39), which contains a list of the Italian paintings handled by the firm (219-223).

62  Letter from Berenson to Edward Fowles, dated June 7, 1934, at I Tatti.

63   Fowles finished his memoirs (see above, n. 39) only up to about 1930. The Metropolitan Museum is the repository of the Duveen archives on which they are based. See also the review in the *Times Literary Supplement,* Mar. 18, 1977, 305.

64   The portraits were purchased for the Kress Collection in 1941 (Shapley, *Italian Schools. XIII-XV Century,* nos. K408-09), pp. 86-87. Three further exchanges between Fowles and the Berensons are worth noting here. In the first, a draft of reply, Mary Berenson wrote Fowles on Dec. 19, 1924, as follows:

> Your letter of the 16th. has just come. It puts B.B. again into the embarrassing position of refusing to do what Sir Joseph desires—that is to say, writing articles to crack up pictures that the Firm wants to sell, or has just sold. Now we are sure that this would *end fatally;* it could not help looking as if his pen was at the service of his interests, like Venturi's and so many others. And that is a thing he has always been most careful to avoid. . . .
>
> For the benefit of the Firm (not to speak of B.B.'s position) it is surely a hundred times better in the long run to command the opinion of an independent scholar, who works on his own lines and not to order. In the short run, no doubt, it would be helpful to this or that sale for B.B. to write it up, but in the end we should all lose by it. Besides, it is a thing he cannot do, for his mind does not work that way. If he did it, it would be inferior work, and what good would that do to any of us?

At this time Fowles was attempting to get Berenson to change his mind about a Raphaelesque *Madonna* that Berenson had refused to attribute to the master (letter to Mary, Dec. 23, 1924). She replied on Dec. 26 (her draft preserved, like the former one, at I Tatti): "Everything you say about the picture would be perfect criticism if the picture were what it only imitates, if it were a Raphael. . . . You can imagine that [B.B.] wanted to think it was by that Master quite as much as you can want it! He naturally would have greatly preferred getting the profit that would have accrued to him, if he only could have passed it as a Raphael. . . . B.B. remains quite unshaken in his belief that it is not Raphael, in spite of all the qualities you mention." Mary continued,

> The second important point in your letter is about B.B.'s writing articles for pictures that are for sale, and *überhaupt* writing to order. Believe me, these are two things he has never done and really *cannot do.* The first would be fatal to his reputation; the second, to his talent. His gifts, such as they are, have always developed along their own lines and at their own time, and really, dear Mr Edward, which makes him different from all the other writers on Italian art. It is this which enables him to take rank not only as a connoisseur but as a scholar and humanist. No one who has not gone around with him can have any idea of the respect with which he is everywhere received by learned men of all kinds. It would be entirely different if they could write off his opinions as depending on what he made out of them, or if they did not recognize that when he wrote anything it was because he was in exactly the phase when his interest was directed upon that subject. This liberty of development, of going his own way, as the subjects in which he is interested lead him, he prizes more than money.

The third letter of Mar. 24, 1927, Mary said, was the outcome of their deliberations over one sent by Fowles on Mar. 22, 1927. In a draft of reply at I Tatti, she recapitulated B.B.'s position:

> . . . he is absolutely convinced that it would be a mistake to sacrifice his general principles to a temporary advantage. He has calculated his conduct with a view to the whole of his career and to that of the Firm. He is not willing to have letters of his go the rounds of the trade; he is not willing to include in his ultimate lists pictures which he knows to be in the market.
>
> I hope, when you look at it all round, you will see that this policy is wise. Any other course would cheapen the value of his word and besides, it would bring scorn and ridicule on the whole affair, for everyone knows that this has been his policy for thirty years.
>
> All the same, we understand fully the position you are in which makes you urge him upon another course and it is not easy to stick by one's considered principles in opposition to you. But we are both convinced that it is the best course *for us all* in the long run.

65   See Alastair Smart, "Roger Fry and Early Italian Art," in *Apollo, 133,* no. 50 (Apr. 1966): 262-271.

66   Letter of Fry to Mary Berenson, May 10, 1902, at I Tatti (published in Sutton, ed., *Letters, 1:* 208-209).

67   See Sutton, *Letters, 1:* 10-13, 15, 18, 22, 63.

68   Told by G. M. Richter in "Lost and Rediscovered Works by Giorgione. Part I," *Art in America, 30,* no. 3 (July 1942): 161.

69   *Venetian School, 1:* 85, 192.

70   In about 1490 an agent of the duke of Milan reported to his master about the work of four famous painters active in Florence: Botticelli, Filippino Lippi, Perugino, and Ghirlandaio. His account, still preserved, was not simply an exercise in art appreciation, rather the painters were being recommended for employment. With the duke in Milan and the artists in Florence, a sort of connoisseurship was required. The document was discovered in the Archivio di Stato, Milan, by Paul Müller-Walde ("Beitrage zur Kenntnis des Leonardo da Vinci," in *Jahrbuch der königlich preussischen Kunstsammlungen, 28* [1897]: 113-114, 165). It has often been reprinted; see Herbert Horne, *Sandro Botticelli* (London, 1908), 109-110, 353. The Venetian Marcantonio Michiel (d. 1552) was a remarkably acute observer of works of art in north Italy. He recorded his observations in a diary (see Robert Klein and Henri Zerner, *Italian Art 1500-1600. Sources and Documents* [Englewood Cliffs, N.J., 1966], 25-30). In doing so, he distinguished among different artists' manners and originals from copies. He even tried to identify the shares of artists working in collaboration. But Michiel was concerned with paintings which were nearly contemporary and of which he evidently had some direct knowledge, so that he does not, strictly speaking, qualify as a connoisseur of the art of the past.

71   Mantegna, Gian Gristoforo Romano, and the sculptor called

L'Antico were all asked by Isabella d'Este to authenticate antiquities for her collection (Clifford M. Brown, "'Lo Insaciable Desiderio Nostro de Cose Antique': New Documents on Isabella d'Este's Collection of Antiquities," in *Cultural Aspects of the Italian Renaissance, Essays in Honour of Paul Oskar Kristeller,* ed. Cecil H. Clough (Manchester, 1976), 333-335 [324-353]. To facilitate comparison, she exhibited Michelangelo's famous *Sleeping Cupid* opposite an antique version ascribed to Praxiteles (Clifford M. Brown, "The Grotta of Isabella d'Este," *Gazette des Beaux-Arts, 139* (May-June 1977): 162-163 [155-713]. On the artist as connoisseur in antiquity see the anecdote about Protogenes and Apelles in J. J. Pollitt, *The Art of Greece 1400-31 B.C. Sources and Documents* (Englewood Cliffs, N.J., 1965), 164.

72  Quoted in translation from Giorgio Vasari, *Le Vite de' Più Eccellenti Pittori, Scultori ed Architettori, 7,* ed. Gaetano Milanesi (Florence, 1881): 727. About Vasari as connoisseur see the brief remarks in Lionello Venturi, *History of Art Criticism,* trans. Charles Marriott (New York, 1936), 103-109; and Evert van der Grinten, *Enquiries into the History of Art-Historical Writing* (Venlo, 1952), 36-37.

73  Vasari noted that the young Signorelli imitated his teacher, Piero della Francesca, so closely that their works could hardly be told apart (*Vite, 3* [1878]: 683-684). Lorenzo di Credi successfully copied Verrocchio and his fellow pupil Leonardo (*Vite, 4* [1879]: 564-566). Raffaellino del Garbo had acquired Filippino Lippi's manner so well that there were few who could distinguish their works (*Vite, 4* [1879]: 235). Even Giorgione's friends were unable to differentiate his paintings from the early Titian's (*Vite, 7* [1881]: 428-429). On the other hand, Sebastiano del Piombo's altarpiece for San Giovanni Crisostomo was taken for Giorgione's by persons who, according to Vasari, had little acquaintance with matters of art (*Vite, 5* [1880]: 565-566). The expert was Raphael, whose youthful works differed scarcely, if at all, from Perugino's (*Vite, 4* [1878]: 317). Vasari cited the *Coronation of the Virgin,* now in the Vatican Pinacoteca, as an example. He claimed that if Raphael had not signed the *Crucifixion* (National Gallery, London), anyone without a thorough knowledge of Perugino's style would assume it was by that master. Only in the *Marriage of the Virgin* (Brera) did Raphael's superiority become evident (pp. 318-319).

74  See the review by Berenson of the 1896 edition of Mrs. Foster's translation of Vasari's *Vite* (edited by E. H. and E. W. Blashfield and A. A. Hopkins) in *The Nation, 114* (Mar. 25, 1897): 227-228.

75  Vasari's collection of drawings has been reconstituted by Licia Ragghianti Collobi in *Il Libro de' Disegni del Vasari,* 2 vols. (Florence, 1974). See also Roseline Bacou, *Giorgio Vasari Dessinateur et Collectioneur,* exh. cat. Musée du Louvre (Paris, 1965).

76  See A. E. Popham and Philip Pouncey, *Italian Drawings in the Department of Prints and Drawings in the British Museum. The Fourteenth and Fifteenth Centuries* (London, 1950), *1:* cat. nos. 61-62, pp. 42-43.

77  Though not a practicing artist, Filippo Baldinucci (1625-1696) followed in Vasari's mold of the collector as connoisseur. He also shared Vasari's biographical approach to art history. A new feature of his connoisseurship, however, was his role as advisor to Cardinal Leopoldo de' Medici, by whom he was employed to gather and inventory a vast number of drawings that formed the nucleus of the holdings of the Uffizi Gallery. About Baldinucci, see: Roseline Bacou and Jacob Bean, *Disegni Fiorentini del Museo del Louvre dalla Collezione di Filippo Baldinucci,* exh. cat. (Rome, 1959; French ed., 1958). Baldinucci's connoisseurship, like that of his Milanese contemporary Padre Sebastiano Resta, seems rudimentary by comparison with that of the eighteenth century. For the emergence of the term "connoisseur," see *The Oxford English Dictionary, 2* (1933): 840.

78  About Rowlandson's drawing in the Paul Mellon Collection at the Yale Center for British Art, see: John Baskett and Dudley Snelgrove, *The Drawings of Thomas Rowlandson in the Paul Mellon Collection* (New York, 1978), cat. no. 194, p. 51; and John Riely, *Rowlandson Drawings from the Paul Mellon Collection,* exh. cat. (1977-1978), cat. no. 37, pp. 27-28. Rowlandson explored the theme of the connoisseur looking at works of art in a whole series of prints and drawings (Ronald Paulson, *Rowlandson, A New Interpretation* [New York, 1972], 83-85). For a modern attack on connoisseurship see Harry Hahn, *The Rape of La Belle* (Kansas City, Mo., 1946). The polemic was occasioned by the notorious Hahn-Duveen trial, in which various experts, including Berenson, were called upon to testify about the attribution to Leonardo of a painting owned by Hahn.

79  About the remarks on connoisseurship of Félibien (1666-88), Roger de Piles (1677, 1699), d'Argenville (1745-52), the comte de Caylus (1752-67), and Richardson Senior (1719), see: van der Grinten, *Art-Historical Writing,* 53-54, 55-56, 59-60, 68, 72-73.

80  The original 1719 text of the *Two Discourses* has been reprinted by the Scolar Press, Menston, Yorkshire, England, 1972. Quotations are from this edition. *An Account of Some of the Statues, Basreliefs, Drawings, and Pictures in Italy* (London, 1722) shows how conventional was Richardson's taste.

81  "Art of Criticism" from *Two Discourses,* 23.

82  "Art of Criticism" from *Two Discourses,* 102-103.

83  About Mariette, a book and print seller as well as collector, see principally Frits Lugt, *Les Marques de Collections de Dessins et d'Estampes* (Amsterdam, 1921), no. 1852; and Roseline Bacou, *Le Cabinet d'un Grand Amateur, P.-J. Mariette 1694-1774,* exh. cat., Musée du Louvre (Paris, 1967). It is typical of his dual nature as collector and connoisseur that Mariette scrupulously prepared the sale catalogue (1741) of drawings amassed by his friend, the financier Pierre Crozat, and then acquired the best sheets for himself. For some other early Italian drawings owned by Mariette see: Popham and Pouncey, *Italian Drawings . . . The Fourteenth and Fifteenth Centuries, 1:* cat. nos. 20, 47, 60 (also Vasari), 88 (also Vasari), 107, 131 (also Vasari), 179, and 188 (also Vasari). Also, Bacou, *Le Cabinet,* cat. nos. 20, 23 (also Vasari), 49 (also Vasari), 50, 55 (also Vasari), 56 (also Vasari), 64 (also Vasari), 66, 74, 75, 78 (also Vasari), and 101 (also Vasari); Walter Koschatzky, Konrad Oberhuber, and Eckhart Knab, *I Grandi Disegni Italiani dell'Albertina di Vienna* (Milan [c. 1972]), cat. nos. 7 (also Vasari), 8 (also Vasari), 13, and 14 (also Vasari).

84   This suggestion was made by Jacob Bean. See: E. Tietze-Conrat, "Decorative Paintings of the Venetian Renaissance Reconstructed from Drawings," *The Art Quarterly*, 3, no. 1 (1940): 31-32 (15-39); and Hans Tietze and E. Tietze-Conrat, *The Drawings of the Venetian Painters in the 15th and 16th Centuries* (New York, 1944), cat. no. 712, p. 174. A marginal sketch of this drawing by Gabriel de Saint-Aubin is found in the annotated copy of the Mariette sale catalogue of 1775 (whence the Giorgione attribution), preserved in the Museum of Fine Arts, Boston. Mariette may have had in mind the nude female figure in a niche from the Fondaco decoration, as it appears engraved in Anton Maria Zanetti's *Varie Pitture a Fresco* (Venice, 1760), pl. 3 (conveniently reproduced in Terisio Pignatti, *Giorgione* [Venice, 1971], fig. 55).

85   About Jarves see: Francis Steegmuller, *The Two Lives of James Jackson Jarves* (New Haven, 1951); and about his collection, *Italian Primitives. The Case History of a Collection and its Conservation*, exh. cat., Yale University Art Gallery (New Haven, 1972). Berenson said he "had a cult of [Jarves] as the first American who wrote discriminatingly about Italian painting" (letter to Francis Steegmuller of Nov. 25, 1944, at I Tatti). Berenson explained, however, that his interest in Jarves as a predecessor postdated his own pioneering research (letter to Francis Steegmuller, Nov. 9, 1949, at I Tatti).

86   James Jackson Jarves, *Art Studies. The "Old Masters" of Italy. Painting* (New York-London, 1861), 33-52. The chapter on connoisseurship provides a colorful account of the Italian art market and of the faking of old masters.

87   *Descriptive Catalogue of "Old Masters" Collected by James J. Jarves to Illustrate the History of Painting from A.D. 1200 to the Best Periods of Italian Art* (Cambridge, Mass., 1863), no. 65, pp. 15-16 (1st ed. 1860). For the present attribution see Seymour, *Yale University Art Gallery*, cat. no. 173, p. 230.

88   About Crowe and Cavalcaselle see: Crowe, *Reminiscences of Thirty-Five Years of my Life* (London, 1895); Lino Moretti, *G. B. Cavalcaselle. Disegni da Antichi Maestri*, exh. cat., Cini Foundation (Venice, 1973); and Francis Haskell, *Rediscoveries in Art. Some Aspects of Taste, Fashion and Collecting in England and France*, The Wrightsman Lectures (Ithaca, N.Y., 1976), 91-92. Crowe, an English journalist, joined forces at mid-century with Cavalcaselle, an exiled Italian patriot also trained as an artist. Back in Italy, Cavalcaselle was commissioned to compile inventories of works of art in various regions, and these he turned to account in the surveys he prepared with Crowe. Their collaboration resulted in *A New History of Painting in Italy*, first published in three volumes in 1864-1866 and continued as *A History of Painting in North Italy* in two volumes in 1871. Significantly, Crowe and Cavalcaselle focused on hitherto neglected artists; and though they planned separate monographs about the great High Renaissance masters, only two were ever completed, one on Titian in 1877 and another on Raphael five years later. Their thousands of annotated sketch copies are in the Victoria and Albert Museum in London and the Biblioteca Marciana in Venice.

89   For their meeting see: *Italienische Malerei der Renaissance im Briefwechsel von Giovanni Morelli und Jean Paul Richter 1876-1891*, ed. Irma and Gisela Richter (Baden-Baden, 1960), 583-584. Though Clark may be wrong that Berenson only saw Morelli once or twice (*Burlington Magazine*, 102: 382), Berenson did complain that "I can't really speak to Morelli because he expects to be treated en maître" (letter to Mary of Feb. 13, 1891, in *Selected Letters*, 4). About Berenson and Morelli see also the letter to Mary of Nov. 2, 1890, printed in *Berenson Treasury*, 44.

90   A Morelli bibliography is appended to *Briefwechsel*, 583-584. About Morelli himself see the biographical introduction of his disciple, Austen Henry Layard, to his *Italian Painters. Critical Studies of their Works. The Borghese and Doria-Pamfili Galleries*, trans. Constance Jocelyn Ffoulkes (London, 1892), intro. pp. 1-39.

91   *Borghese and Doria-Pamfili Galleries*, 20. The quotations are from the fundamental chapter "Principles and Methods."

92   *Italian Painters. Critical Studies of their Works. The Galleries of Munich and Dresden*, trans. Constance Jocelyn Ffoulkes (London, 1893), 148 (1st ed.: Leipzig, 1891, p. 196). Morelli first briefly introduced the painting as Correggio's in the *Zeitschrift für bildende Kunst*, 10 (1875): 332. The picture, which belonged to his disciple, Gustavo Frizzoni, is also discussed in the Morelli-Richter correspondence (*Briefwechsel*, 6-8, 16-17, 43, 48, 76, 360, 419, 449).

93   Max J. Friedländer, the foremost connoisseur of northern European painting, claimed that the method Morelli devised was a pseudo-scientific justification for results obtained by a process that was more personal and intuitive than he admitted (*On Art and Connoisseurship*, trans. Tancred Borenius [Boston, 1960], 166-167, 170 [orig. German ed. 1919]). Edgar Wind reaffirmed the validity of Morelli's principles in *Art and Anarchy* (New York, 1964), pp. 32-51 (also in *Art News*, 63, no. 1 [Mar. 1964]: 26-29, 52-55). The most balanced critique of the Morellian method is by W. G. Constable in *Art History and Connoisseurship* (Cambridge, 1938), 33-47. Morelli's investigative method has recently been compared to those of Sherlock Holmes and Freud by Carlo Ginzburg ("Spie. Radici di un Paradigma Scientifico," *Rivista di Storia Contemporanea*, no. 1 [1978], 1-14). See also the stimulating analysis of Richard Wollheim in *On Art and the Mind* (London, 1973), 177-201; and of Henri Zerner, "Giovanni Morelli et la science de l'art," *Revue de l'Art*, nos. 40-41 [1978], 209-215.

94   No complete account of the rediscovery of the earlier Italian schools has yet been attempted, though there are the following: Camillo von Klenze, "The Growth of Interest in the Early Italian Masters," in *Modern Philology*, 4, no. 2 (Oct. 1906): 207-274; Tancred Borenius, "The Rediscovery of the Primitives," *The Quarterly Review*, 239, no. 475 (Apr. 1923): 258-270; Lionello Venturi, *Il Gusto dei Primitivi* (Bologna, 1926), esp. 135-182; J. R. Hale, *England and the Italian Renaissance* (London, 1954), 60-83, 108-126, 149-168; André Chastel, "Le Gout des 'Préraphaélites' en France," in *De Giotto à Bellini. Les Primitifs Italiens dans les Musées de France*, ed. Michelle Laclotte, exh. cat., Musée de l'Orangerie (Paris, 1956), vii-xxi (translated in *Paragone*, 79 [July 1956]: 3-16); E. K. Waterhouse, *Italian Art and Britain*, exh. cat., Royal Academy (London, 1960); and Denys Sutton, "The English and Early Italian Art," *Apollo*, 131, no. 38 (Apr. 1965): 254-256. Illuminating remarks on the subject are found in Francis Haskell's *Rediscoveries in Art*. As Giovanni Previ-

tali has convincingly shown (*La Fortuna dei Primitivi dal Vasari ai Neoclassici* [Turin, 1964]), the Italians had already begun to recover their medieval past well before the late eighteenth century, but their scholarly interest, verging on *campanilismo*, is not relevant here. The most impressive instance of it is that of Luigi Lanzi, *Storia Pittorica della Italia* (Florence, 1789), with many later editions.

95   About Seroux d'Agincourt see: M. Lamy, "La Découverte des Primitifs Italiens au XIXe Siècle. Seroux d'Agincourt et son Influence sur les Collectionneurs, Critiques et Artistes Français," *Revue de l'art Ancien et Moderne*, 39, no. 1 (1921): 169-181, and no. 2 (1921): 182-190; and Previtali, *Fortuna dei Primitivi*, 164-175. About Artaud de Montor see: Previtali, *Fortuna dei Primitivi*, 185-187. About other French holdings of early Italian pictures see Michel Laclotte and Elizabeth Mongetti, *Peinture Italienne. Musée de Petit Palais, Avignon* (Paris, 1976). Ignatius Hugford may have been buying early paintings in Italy already in the mid-eighteenth century; see John Fleming, "The Hugfords of Florence. Part II," *The Connoisseur*, 136, no. 549 (Dec. 1955): 197-206. In de Montor's catalogue (of which the introduction had already been published in 1808 and again in 1811), the painting is no. 115 and pl. 49. Berenson's opinion is recorded on a letter from Duveen Brothers dated May 26, 1936, at I Tatti.

96   In de Montor's *Peintres Primitifs* (Paris, 1843), of which the introduction had already been published in 1808 and again in 1811, the painting is no. 115 and pl. 49. Berenson's opinion is recorded on a letter from Duveen Brothers dated May 26, 1936, at I Tatti.

97   See de Montor, *Peintres Primitifs*, cat. nos. 35-38, pp. 30-31. Of the other two lateral panels, one is missing and the *St. John the Baptist* is at Chambéry (*Primitifs Italiens*, exh. cat. [1956], cat. no. 20, p. 15). For Berenson's item see: "A Newly Discovered Cimabue," *Art in America*, 8, no. 6 (Oct. 1920): 251-271 (republished in *Studies in Medieval Painting*, 17-31); and for the revision, Roberto Longhi, "Giudizio sul Duecento" (1939) in *Opere Complete*, 7 (Florence, 1974), 14-15. Another National Gallery painting that figured in the rediscovery of the Italian primitives was Francesco Benaglio's *St. Jerome*, which belonged to the Liverpool banker and historian of the Medici, William Roscoe (1753-1831). About Roscoe see Michael Compton, "William Roscoe and Early Collectors of Italian Primitives," *Liverpool Bulletin*, 9, Walker Art Gallery (1960/61): 26-51.

98   About the brotherhood of German painters in Rome who, early in the nineteenth century, sought to recapture in their art the mystic spirit of the Middle Ages, see Keith Andrews, *The Nazarenes* (Oxford, 1964). Their chief model, however, was Raphael, whose early work was classed with that of the primitives.

99   Alexis François Rio, *The Poetry of Christian Art* (London, 1854). For Angelico and Perugino, who belonged to the mystic school, see respectively pp. 146-153 and 162-183. Both *De la Poésie Chrétienne* (Paris, 1836), and *De l'Art Chrétien* (Paris, 1851), of which the English edition is comprised, deal with Italian art. About Rio see von Klenze, "Early Italian Masters," 256-269.

58

100   *Sketches of the History of Christian Art*, 3 vols. (London, 1847). See John Steegman, "Lord Lindsay's 'History of Christian Art'," in *Journal of the Warburg and Courtauld Institutes*, 10 (1947): 123-131.

101   Mrs. Jameson, according to Nathaniel Hawthorne, could read a picture like the page of a book (*Passages from the French and Italian Notebooks*. 1 [Boston, 1899]: 185). Ruskin, who disapproved of Mrs. Jameson said she "knows as much about art as the cat"(*Ruskin in Italy. Letters to his Parents 1845*, ed. Harold I. Shapiro [Oxford, 1972], no. 136).

102   *The Works of John Ruskin*, ed. by E. T. Cook and Alexander Wedderburn, 39 vols. (London, 1903-1912).

103   *The Oxford English Dictionary*, 8 (Oxford, 1933): 1366.

104   *One Year's Reading for Fun (1942)* (New York, 1960), p. 12.

105   Review of William White, *The Principles of Art as Illustrated in the Ruskin Museum*, in *The Studio* 8, no. 42 (1896): 249.

106   *Pitture a Fresco del Campo Santo di Pisa, Intagliate dal Professore Cav. Carlo Lasinio, Conservatore del Medesimo* (Florence, 1828). This edition of Lasinio's book consists of forty plates after frescoes, half of which are by Gozzoli. About its influence on the Pre-Raphaelites see William Holman Hunt, *Pre-Raphaelitism and the Pre-Raphaelite Brotherhood*, 1 (New York, 1905): 130, 133 (2nd ed.: New York, 1914, pp. 19, 12); and William Michael Rossetti, *Dante Gabriel Rossetti. His Family Letters with a Memoir* (London, 1895), 125-126.

107   Much has been written recently about Burne-Jones and Italy. See: Martin Harrison and Bill Waters, *Burne-Jones* (London, 1973), *passim*; Ronald Parkinson, "Two Early Altar-Pieces by Burne-Jones," *Apollo*, 102 (Nov. 1975): 320-323; John Christian, "Burne-Jones' Second Italian Journey," *Apollo*, 102 (Nov. 1975): 334-337; and Duncan Robinson, "Burne-Jones, Fairfax Murray and Siena," *Apollo*, 102 (Nov. 1975): 348-351.

108   About the album, no. 1084 in the Fitzwilliam Museum, Cambridge, see: *Burne-Jones, The Paintings, Graphic and Decorative Work*, exh. cat., Hayward Gallery (London, 1975), cat. no. 333, p. 91.

109   *North Italian Painters of the Renaissance*, 50-51; *Sunset and Twilight*, 480-481 (diary entry, May 24, 1957).

110   About Norton see: Kermit Vanderbilt, *Charles Eliot Norton. Apostle of Culture in a Democracy* (Cambridge, Mass., 1959); and Roger B. Stein, *John Ruskin and Aesthetic Thought in America, 1840-1900* (Cambridge, Mass., 1967), 240-254. Compare also the subtle penetrating tribute by Henry James in *The Burlington Magazine*, 14, no. 70 (Jan. 1909): 201-204.

111   The incident is recounted in Mary Berenson's "Unpublished Life," (unpublished ms., on deposit at I Tatti), chap. 2.

112   *Sunset and Twilight*, 23 (diary entry for June 25, 1947). Compare Berenson's *Self-Portrait*, 44-45; and *One Year's Reading*, 131.

113   Berenson evidently did meet Pater sometime between his stay at Oxford in 1888 and Pater's death in 1894 (*Sunset and Twilight,* 343). While he continued to read Pater all his life (*Self-Portrait,* 129; *One Year's Reading, passim*), it is worth noting that in the copy of *The Renaissance,* lent to the exhibition by I Tatti, Berenson noted on Mar. 28, 1942, that he read the notorious conclusion for the first time since 1888. For an acutely perceptive modern reading of Pater's work, both essays and fiction, see Richard L. Stein, *The Ritual of Interpretation. The Fine Arts as Literature in Ruskin, Rossetti, and Pater* (Cambridge, Mass., 1975).

114   Rediscovered in the early nineteenth century, Botticelli became a cult figure, especially in England, where his works were extravagantly admired (Michael Levey, "Botticelli and Nineteenth-Century England," *Journal of the Warburg and Courtauld Institutes,* 23, nos. 3-4 [July-December 1960]: 291-306). It was from the Pre-Raphaelites that Pater too learned to love the artist, publishing a "Fragment" on him in the *Fortnightly Review* for 1870 that was included in the first edition of the *Renaissance* three years later. For the young Berenson on Botticelli see the letter to Mary Costelloe, from Florence, Jan. 1892, quoted in *Selected Letters,* 12, 13; and in *Looking at Pictures,* 182; *The Passionate Sightseer—from the Diaries of 1947 to 1956* (London, 1960), 176-177; and *Looking at Pictures,* 184.

115   Letter of Oct. 9, 1890, quoted in "Unpublished life," chap. 2.

116   Quoted in Mary Berenson's "Unpublished Life," chap. 2, and in part in *Looking at Pictures,* 314. In a book review Pope-Hennessy has suggested that Berenson would not have stood by his fanciful identification of the sitter (*Times Literary Supplement,* May 28, 1976, 640).

117   *Self-Portrait,* 50-51. Berenson's companion was Enrico Costa (1867-1911).

118   About the issue of quality see: Jacob Rosenberg, *On Quality in Art. Criteria of Excellence Past and Present,* A. W. Mellon Lectures in the Fine Arts, Princeton, 1964; the review by E. H. Gombrich in *The New York Review of Books,* Feb. 1, 1968, 5-7; and Sherman E. Lee, "Painting," in *Quality. Its Image in the Arts,* ed. Louis Kronenberger (New York, 1969), 113-45.

119   *The Study and Criticism of Italian Art* (1901), vi-viii.

120   See his *Three Essays.* The articles about Domenico Morone, Botticelli, and Antonello da Messina appeared in *Dedalo* in 1923-1925. The preface to the book contains the celebrated aphorism "In the beginning was the guess" (p. ix).

121   Compare, for example, "Two Twelfth-Century Paintings from Constantinople," first published in *Dedalo,* Oct. 1921, and reprinted in *Studies in Medieval Painting,* 1-31. The collected studies date from 1913 to 1926. The article cited concerns two Byzantine Madonnas now in the National Gallery (nos. 1, 1048).

122   About this master see *Homeless Paintings,* 184-187 (reprinted in translation from *Dedalo,* 12 [1932]).

123   For details about this master see Zeri, *Walters Art Gallery,* 1: 100-103. Berenson first identified him in *Burlington Magazine,* 1, no. 1 (Mar. 1903): 6-20.

124   See *Study and Criticism* (1901), 46-69 (reprinted from *Gazette des Beaux-Arts,* 1898, 459-471; 1899, 21-36); and the 3rd rev. ed. of the *Florentine Painters of the Renaissance with an Index to Their Works* (1909), 100-101.

125   In a notebook on collections in and near Paris of 1895, Berenson registered one item as "Author of Morte di Lucrezia," while Mary added "Amico di Sandro". In another notebook of 1896 she related the National Gallery's *Portrait of a Youth* (no. 20), when it was in the Liechtenstein Collection, to the "Morte di Lucrezia."

126   Compare *Berenson's Treasury,* 57 (letter to Mary, of Jan. 19, 1900).

127   "Unpublished Life," chap. 3.

128   "Unpublished Life," chap. 9.

129   *The Studio,* 8, no. 41 (1896): 181-184.

130   M. W. [Mary Whitall], "Pictures in Venice as Documents about Venetian Women," *The Woman's Herald,* Oct. 29, 1892; "The Woman Question in Novels," *The Woman's Herald,* Jan. 7, 1893; "Ibsen's Last Play," *The Woman's Herald,* Feb. 11, 1893.

131   Most of Mary's scholarly articles, signed "Mary Logan" and then "Mary Logan Berenson," appeared in the *Revue Archeologique* and *Rassegna d'Arte* from about 1900 to 1915, but others, such as "The New and the Old Art Criticism," *The Nineteenth Century,* May 1894, 828-837, date back to the mid-nineties.

132   About the process of revision see the introduction to *Central Italian and North Italian Schools,* 1: ix-xvii. A slightly revised version of the 1932 lists came out in Italian: *Pitture Italiane del Rinascimento* (Milan 1936).

133   Berenson took a deep interest in the photography of art. See his "Isochromatic Photography and Venetian Pictures," *The Nation,* 57 (Nov. 9, 1893): 346-347.

134   "The New Vasari," *The Nation,* 64 (Mar. 25, 1897): 227.

135   *The Venetian Painters of the Renaissance,* 2nd ed. rev. (1895), iii. The same claim was made in the companion volumes on the *Florentine Painters* (1896) and *Central Italian Painters* (1897). By 1907 Berenson's attitude had changed somewhat: compare *North Italian Painters,* v-vi.

136   *Self-Portrait,* 43.

137   See: *Three Essays,* viii; *Aesthetics and History* (London, 1948), 193; and *Sunset and Twilight,* 432.

138   See: Friedländer, *On Art,* 197-199; and Constable, *Connoisseurship,* 13-14.

139  Clark, *Another Part of the Wood,* 152.

140  For Berenson's reports, see *The Nation,* May 10, 1894; Dec. 12, 1895; Jan. 2, 1896; and Feb. 20, 1896. About the Alinari firm see Alessandro Conti, "Storia di una Documentazione," in *Gli Alinari Fotografi a Firenze 1852-1920,* exh. cat. (Florence, 1977), 148-183.

141  See: *Italian Pictures* (1932), 466; *Drawings of the Florentine Painters,* 1: 15-16; and *Florentine School* (London, 1963), 1: 47

142  See: Aaron Scharf, *Art and Photography* (London, 1968), 122-124; and Werner Neile, "G. Schauer: Photograph und Kunst-Verleger in Berlin, 1851-1864," in *History of Photography, 1,* no. 4 (Oct. 1977): 291-296.

143  *Collection of Pictures of W. G. Coesvelt, Esq., of London,* intro. Mrs. Jameson (London, 1836), xii.

144  Other prints after the painting are recorded in J. D. Passavant, *Raphael d'Urbin et son Père Giovanni Santi* (Paris, 1860), 2: 106.

145  *The Nation,* 1893, 346-347. See also on the distortions of reproductive engravings: William M. Ivins, Jr., *Prints and Visual Communication* (Cambridge, Mass., 1953), *passim,* and "A Note on Engraved Reproductions of Works of Art," *in Studies in Art and Literature for Belle da Costa Greene* (Princeton, 1954), 193-196; E. F. van der Grinten, "Consistent Formal Distortions and Peculiarities in 19th Century Art Historical Reproductions. Iconologia Formalis," in *Nederlands Kunsthistorisch Jaarboek,* 15 (1964): 247-260; and Giulio Carlo Argan, "Il Valore Critico della 'Stampa di Traduzione'," in *Essays in the History of Art Presented to Rudolf Wittkower* (London, 1967), 179-181.

146  *The Nation,* 1893, 346-347.

147  The continuing popularity of engravings and chromolithographs is attested by the Arundel Society (1848-1897), who were active in reproducing works, especially frescoes, by early Italian painters, such as Giotto and Fra Angelico (Alan Bird, "An Earnest Passion for Art—The Arundel Society," *Country Life, 159,* no. 4118 [June 3, 1976]: 1513-1515).

148  *The Nation,* 1893, 346-347. See also Ivins, *Prints,* 116-177. For Ivins photographs were "exactly repeatable pictorial statements about works of art which could be accepted as visual evidence about things other than iconography" (p. 124). For some problems about photography of art works see: Estelle Jussim, *Visual Communication and the Graphic Arts. Photographic Technologies in the Nineteenth Century* (New York-London, 1974), 237-278; and Massimo Ferretti, "Fra Traduzione e Riduzione. La Fotografia dell'Arte come Oggetto e come Modello," in *Gli Alinari Fotografi a Firenze 1852-1920,* exh. cat. (Florence, 1977), 116-147.

149  *Ad. Braun & Cie. Catalogue Général des Photographies Inalterables au Charbon et Heliogravures Faites d'après les Originaux Peintures, Fresques, Dessins et Sculptures des Principaux Musées en Europe, les Galeries et Collections Particulières les Plus Remarquables* (Paris, 1887), no. 38, p. 177. I am grateful to Prof. Peter Bunnell, who kindly discussed these problems with me.

150  *Three Essays,* 116.

151  The superiority of engravings over the earliest photographs of works of art was cogently argued by Henri Delaborde ("La Photographie et la Gravure (1856)," in *Mélanges sur l'Art Contemporain* [Paris, 1866], 359-388). Improvements in photography rendered reproductive engravings superfluous, however. The last gasp of the long tradition of engraving art works, as it relates to the "primitives," is Timothy Cole's *Old Italian Masters* (New York, 1892).

152  Quoted in Mary Berenson's "Unpublished Life," chap. 2.

153  Seroux d'Agincourt's plate already included a number of details. See: *History of Art by its Monuments. From its Decline in the Fourth Century to its Restoration in the Sixteenth,* trans. from the French of Seroux d'Agincourt (London, 1847). Plate 139 shows details of the head, hand, and foot of Mantegna's *St. Euphemia.*

154  Berenson in 1892 referred to a large photograph of the head of the *Primavera* as "very beautiful by itself" (*Selected Letters,* 1).

155  Ivins, *Prints,* 136.

156  *Aesthetics and History,* London, 1948, p. 190.

157  *Italian Painting,* 1952, p. x.

158  Letter from Mary Berenson to Isabella Stewart Gardner, dated Jan. 19, 1921, at Fenway Court. See also the letter of the same day from Berenson to Paul Sachs, quoted in *Selected Letters,* 89.

159  "A Boticelli Portrait in the Collection of Carl W. Hamilton," *Art in America, 10,* no. 1 (Dec. 1921): 26-30.

# CHECKLIST

Dimensions are given in meters (inches); height precedes width.

Antonello da Messina    Sicilian, active 1456-1479

1  *Madonna and Child*
Wood, 0.59 x 0.44 (23¼ x 17¼ in)

National Gallery of Art, Washington
Andrew W. Mellon Collection 1937

2  *Bernard Berenson as a Harvard Student,* 1887
Photograph
Pach Brothers Photo, Cambridge, Massachusetts

Villa I Tatti, Harvard University Center for
Italian Renaissance Studies, Florence

3  *Garden Façade of Villa I Tatti*
Photograph made from slide
Dmitri Kessel

Original at *Smithsonian* Magazine, Washington
Copyright Dmitri Kessel 1978

4  *Garden at Villa I Tatti*
Photograph made from slide
Dmitri Kessel

Original at *Smithsonian* Magazine, Washington
Copyright Dmitri Kessel 1978

5  *Garden at Villa I Tatti*
Photograph made from slide
Dmitri Kessel

Original at *Smithsonian* Magazine, Washington
Copyright Dmitri Kessel 1978

6  *Bernard Berenson at Villa I Tatti,* 1903
Photograph
Anonymous

Villa I Tatti, Harvard University Center for
Italian Renaissance Studies, Florence

7  *Bernard Berenson at the Borghese Gallery, Rome,* 1955
Photograph
David Seymour, Magnum Photos

Villa I Tatti, Harvard University Center for
Italian Renaissance Studies, Florence

8  *Library at Villa I Tatti*
Photograph made from slide
Dmitri Kessel

Original at *Smithsonian* Magazine, Washington
Copyright Dmitri Kessel 1978

9  *Interior of Villa I Tatti*
Photograph made from slide
Dmitri Kessel

Original at *Smithsonian* Magazine, Washington
Copyright Dmitri Kessel 1978

10  *Library at Villa I Tatti*
Photograph made from slide
Dmitri Kessel

Original at *Smithsonian* Magazine, Washington
Copyright Dmitri Kessel 1978

Bernard Berenson

11  *The Venetian Painters of the Renaissance with an Index
to Their Works* (New York-London:
G. P. Putnam's Sons, 1906)

National Gallery of Art, Washington

Bernard Berenson

12  *The Florentine Painters of the Renaissance with an Index
to Their Works* (New York-London:
G. P. Putnam's Sons, 1907)

National Gallery of Art, Washington

61

Bernard Berenson

13 *The Central Italian Painters of the Renaissance* (New York-London: G. P. Putnam's Sons, 1907)

National Gallery of Art, Washington

Bernard Berenson

14 *North Italian Painters of the Renaissance* (New York-London: G. P. Putnam's Sons, 1907)

National Gallery of Art, Washington

Bernard Berenson

15 *Venetian Painting Chiefly before Titian at the Exhibition of Venetian Art. The New Gallery, 1895* (London: Vacher & Sons, 1895)

Villa I Tatti, Harvard University Center for Italian Renaissance Studies, Florence

Giorgione   Venetian, c. 1478-1510

16 *The Holy Family*
Transferred from wood to masonite, 0.373 x 0.456 (14⅝ x 17⅞ in)

National Gallery of Art, Washington
Samuel H. Kress Collection 1952

Andrea Mantegna   Paduan, 1431-1506

17 *Judith and Holofernes*
Wood, 0.30 x 0.18 (11⅞ x 7⅛ in)

National Gallery of Art, Washington
Widener Collection 1942

Bernard Berenson

18 *The Drawings of the Florentine Painters, Classified, Criticised and Studied as Documents in the History and Appreciation of Tuscan Art* (New York: E. P. Dutton and Company, 1903)

National Gallery of Art, Washington

Bernard Berenson

19 *Italian Pictures of the Renaissance. A List of the Principal Artists and Their Works with an Index of Places* (Oxford: Clarendon Press, 1932)

National Gallery of Art, Washington

Bernard Berenson

20 *Lorenzo Lotto. An Essay in Constructive Art Criticism* (London: G. Bell & Sons, 1901)

National Gallery of Art, Washington

Lorenzo Lotto   Venetian, c. 1480-1556

21 *A Maiden's Dream*
Wood, 0.43 x 0.34 (16⅞ x 13¼ in)

National Gallery of Art, Washington
Samuel H. Kress Collection 1939

22 *Bernard Berenson*, 1909
Photograph
Anonymous

Villa I Tatti, Harvard University Center for Italian Renaissance Studies, Florence

Mary Berenson   American, 1864-1945

23 *Trip to America*, 1903/1904

Barbara Strachey Halpern, Oxford

24 *Isabella Stewart Gardner*, c. 1905
Photograph
Anonymous

Isabella Stewart Gardner Museum, Boston

25 *Courtyard of Fenway Court*
Photograph made from color transparency
Anonymous

Original at Isabella Stewart Gardner Museum, Boston

26 *Interior of Fenway Court*
Photograph made from color transparency
Anonymous

Original at Isabella Stewart Gardner Museum, Boston

27 *The Jarves Collection Installation*
Photograph reduced from original
Anonymous

Original at Yale University Archives, Yale University Library, New Haven, Connecticut

Follower of Botticelli

28 *Madonna and Child*
Egg tempera on panel, 0.832 x 0.556
(32¾ x 21⅞ in)

Yale University Art Gallery, New Haven,
Connecticut
University Purchase from James Jackson Jarves

Russell Sturgis, Jr.    American, 1836-1909

29 *Manual of the Jarves Collection of Early Italian
Pictures . . .* (New Haven, 1868)

Villa I Tatti, Harvard University Center for
Italian Renaissance Studies, Florence

30 *Aerial View of Lynnewood Hall, Elkins Park,
Pennsylvania*
Photograph enlarged from original
Anonymous

Original at Historical Society of Pennsylvania

31 *Long Gallery at Lynnewood Hall*
Photograph enlarged from lantern slide
Anonymous

Original at National Gallery of Art, Washington

32 *Joseph Widener*
Photograph
Culver Pictures

Culver Pictures Inc., New York

33 *Raphael Room at Lynnewood Hall*
Photograph enlarged from original
Anonymous

National Gallery of Art, Washington

Neroccio de' Landi    Sienese, 1447-1500

34 *Portrait of a Lady,* c. 1490
Wood, 0.465 x 0.305 (18⅜ x 12 in)

National Gallery of Art, Washington
Widener Collection 1942

Honoré Daumier    French, 1808-1879

35 *The Beggars,* c. 1845
Canvas, 0.597 x 0.740 (23½ x 29⅛ in)

National Gallery of Art, Washington
Chester Dale Collection 1962

Andrea del Castagno    Florentine, 1417/19-1457

36 *The Youthful David,* c. 1450
Leather, 1.156 x 0.769 to 0.410 (45½ x 30¼ to
16⅛ in)

National Gallery of Art, Washington
Widener Collection 1942

37 *Pictures in the Collection of P. A. B. Widener at
Lynnewood Hall, Elkins Park, Pennsylvania. Early
Italian and Spanish Schools,* with Biographical and
Descriptive Notes on the Italian Painters by
B. Berenson and on the Spanish Painters by
W. Roberts (Philadelphia, 1916)

National Gallery of Art, Washington

38 *Carl Hamilton*
Photograph
Anonymous

Catherine Hamilton Lancaster and Rita Hamilton
Hager, granddaughters

39 *Carl Hamilton's Apartment in New York*
Photograph
Anonymous

Catherine Hamilton Lancaster and Rita Hamilton
Hager, granddaughters

Domenico Veneziano    Florentine,
active 1438-1461

40 *St. John in the Desert*
Wood, 0.284 x 0.324 (11⅛ x 12¾ in)

National Gallery of Art, Washington
Samuel H. Kress Collection 1943

41 *Letter from Carl Hamilton to the Berensons,* October
19, 1919

Villa I Tatti, Harvard University Center for
Italian Renaissance Studies, Florence

42  *Samuel H. Kress*, 1924
Photograph reduced from original
Pach Brothers, New York

Original at Samuel H. Kress Foundation, New York

Giotto   Florentine, 1266(?)-1337
43  *Madonna and Child*
Wood, 0.855 x 0.620 (33⅝ x 24⅜ in)

National Gallery of Art, Washington
Samuel H. Kress Collection 1939

44  *Newspaper Article by Carlyle Burrows, from "New York
Herald Tribune,"* October 30, 1958

Villa I Tatti, Harvard University Center for
Italian Renaissance Studies, Florence

45  *Telegram from David Finley Concerning the Kress
Collection, with Berenson's Reply,* 1939

Villa I Tatti, Harvard University Center for
Italian Renaissance Studies, Florence

46  *Samuel H. Kress' Apartment, New York*
Photograph
Anonymous
Samuel H. Kress Foundation, New York

47  *Samuel H. Kress' Apartment, New York*
Photograph
Anonymous
Samuel H. Kress Foundation, New York

48  *Samuel H. Kress' Apartment, New York*
Photograph
Anonymous
Samuel H. Kress Foundation, New York

49  *Samuel H. Kress' Apartment, New York*
Photograph
Anonymous
Samuel H. Kress Foundation, New York

50  *Samuel H. Kress' Apartment, New York*
Photograph
Anonymous
Samuel H. Kress Foundation, New York

51  *Bernard Berenson and John Walker, on the Garden Terrace
at Villa I Tatti,* 1939
Photograph
Katie Lewis

Villa I Tatti, Harvard University Center for
Italian Renaissance Studies, Florence

Master of San Miniato   Florentine, active second
half of 15th c.
52  *Madonna and Child*
Tempera on panel, 0.559 x 0.40 (22 x 15¾ in)

Art Gallery, University of Notre Dame, Notre Dame,
Indiana
Gift of Mr. and Mrs. John Walker

53  *Sir Joseph Duveen*
Photograph enlarged from original
Alfredo Valente

Original at National Portrait Gallery, Smithsonian
Institution, Washington

Ercole Roberti   Ferrarese, active 1479-1496
54  *Giovanni II Bentivoglio*
Wood, 0.54 x 0.38 (21⅛ x 15 in)

National Gallery of Art, Washington
Samuel H. Kress Collection 1939

Ercole Roberti   Ferrarese, active 1479-1496
55  *Ginevra Bentivoglio*
Wood, 0.54 x 0.39 (21⅛ x 15¼ in)

National Gallery of Art, Washington
Samuel H. Kress Collection 1939

56  *Letter from Edward Fowles to Bernard Berenson,*
March 29, 1935

Villa I Tatti, Harvard University Center for
Italian Renaissance Studies, Florence

57  *Telegram from Edward Fowles to Bernard Berenson,* 1935

Villa I Tatti, Harvard University Center for
Italian Renaissance Studies, Florence

58  *Roger Fry,* February 27, 1913
Photograph
Alvin Langdon Coburn

Collection of International Museum of
Photography at George Eastman House,
Rochester, New York

59  *Photograph of Bernard Berenson with Roberto
Longhi,* May 8, 1956
Photograph
Foto Locchi

Villa I Tatti, Harvard University Center for
Italian Renaissance Studies, Florence

Giorgione   Venetian, c. 1478-1510

60  *The Adoration of the Shepherds*
Wood, 0.91 x 1.11 (35¼ x 43½ in)

National Gallery of Art, Washington
Samuel H. Kress Collection 1939

61  *Samuel H. Kress' Apartment, New York, with
the Allendale Nativity*
Photograph
Anonymous

Samuel H. Kress Foundation, New York

62  *Bernard Berenson*
Photograph
Dmitri Kessel

Villa I Tatti, Harvard University Center for
Italian Renaissance Studies, Florence

63  *Portrait of Giorgio Vasari in "Le Vite de Più
Eccellenti Pittori, Scultori ed Architettori,"* by
Giorgio Vasari (Florence: Giunti, 1568)

National Gallery of Art, Washington

Attributed to Piero di Cosimo   Florentine,
1462-c.1521

64  *Sheet of Studies of the Madonna and Child and
Other Figures*
Pen and ink and wash, 0.245 x 0.183
(9⅝ x 7³⁄₁₆ in)

Trustees of the British Museum, London

Raffaellino del Garbo   Florentine, 1470-1524(?)

65  *Study of Hands and a Sleeve*
Metalpoint on pinkish prepared surface, heightened
with white, 0.208 x 0.145  (8³⁄₁₆ x 5¹¹⁄₁₆ in)

Trustees of the British Museum, London

Thomas Rowlandson   English, 1756-1827

66  *The Connoisseurs*
Pen and watercolor over pencil, on wove paper,
0.229 x 0.308 (9 x 12⅛ in)

Yale Center for British Art, New Haven,
Connecticut
Paul Mellon Collection

Jonathan Richardson   English, 1665-1745

67  *Two Discourses* (London, 1719)

Princeton University Library, Princeton, New
Jersey

Augustin de Saint-Aubin (after Cochin)   French,
1736-1807

68  *Pierre-Jean Mariette,* 1765
Engraving, 0.192 x 0.143 (7⁹⁄₁₆ x 5⅝ in)

The Metropolitan Museum of Art, New York
Harris Brisbane Dick Fund, 1917

Giorgione(?)   Venetian, c. 1478-1510

69  *Cupid Bending a Bow*
Red chalk on brown paper, 0.165 x 0.064
(6½ x 2½ in)

The Metropolitan Museum of Art, New York
Rogers Fund, 1911

Larkin Goldsmith Mead   American, 1835-1910

70  *James Jackson Jarves,* 1883
Bronze plaque, 0.426 x 0.33 (16¾ x 13 in)

Yale University Art Gallery, New Haven, Connecticut

Gift of Mrs. Walter Raleigh Kerr

71  *Plate from "Art Studies. The 'Old Masters' of Italy.
Painting,"* by James Jackson Jarves (New York-
London, 1861)

Marquand Library, Princeton University,
Princeton, New Jersey

Fiorenzo di Lorenzo    Umbrian, 1440-1521

72    *St. Jerome*
Egg tempera on panel, 0.486 x 0.305
(19⅛ x 12 in)

Yale University Art Gallery, New Haven,
Connecticut
University Purchase from James Jackson Jarves

Franz von Lenbach    German, 1836-1904

73    *Giovanni Morelli,* 1886
Oil on canvas, 1.30 x 0.94 (51⅛ x 37 in)

Accademia Carrara di Belle Arti, Bergamo

Giovanni Morelli    Italian, 1816-1891

74    *Page from a Notebook of a Journey to the Marches with
Cavalcaselle,* 1861

Anonymous lender

Giovanni Morelli    Italian, 1816-1891

75    *Sheet of Drawings of Four Monkeys' Skulls*
Pen and ink, 0.145 x 0.197 (5¹¹⁄₁₆ x 7¾ in)

Anonymous lender

66

Johann Baptist von Spix    German, 1781-1826

76    *Cephalogenesis, sive capitis ossei structura formatio,
et significatio per omnes animalium classes, familias
genera ac aetates digesta, atque tabulis illustrata,
legesque simul phychologae, cranioscopiae, ac
physignomiae indederivata* (Munich, 1815)

National Library of Medicine, Bethesda, Maryland

Giovanni Morelli    Italian, 1816-1891

77    *Page from "Italian Painters. Critical Studies of Their
Works. The Borghese and Doria-Pamfili Galleries in
Rome,"* trans. Constance Jocelyn Ffoulkes
(London, 1892)

Fine Arts Library, Harvard University, Cambridge,
Massachusetts

Giovanni Morelli    Italian, 1816-1891

78    *Page from "Italian Painters. Critical Studies of Their
Works. The Borghese and Doria-Pamfili Galleries in
Rome,"* trans. Constance Jocelyn Ffoulkes
(London, 1900)

National Gallery of Art, Washington

Correggio    School of Parma, 1489/94-1534

79    *The Mystic Marriage of St. Catherine*
Wood, 0.277 x 0.213 (10⅞ x 8⅜ in)

National Gallery of Art, Washington
Samuel H. Kress Collection 1939

80    *Pages from "Peintres Primitifs," by Artaud de
Montor* (Paris, 1843)

Villa I Tatti, Harvard University Center for
Italian Renaissance Studies, Florence

Attributed to Cimabue    Florentine, active c. 1272-1302

81    *Christ between St. Peter and St. James Major,* soon
after 1270
Wood; center panel, 0.79 x 0.55 (31 x 21¾ in); left panel,
0.68 x 0.36 (26¾ x 14¼ in); right panel, 0.66 x 0.36
(26 x 14¼ in)

National Gallery of Art, Washington
Andrew W. Mellon Collection 1937

82    *Portrait of Anna Brownell Jameson in "Sacred and
Legendary Art," vol. 1,* by Anna Brownell Jameson
(Boston—New York, 1895)

Library of Congress, Washington

83    *Plate from "Legends of the Madonna as Represented
in the Fine Arts,"* by Anna Brownell Jameson
(London, 1891)

National Gallery of Art, Washington

Pietro Perugino    Umbrian, probably 1445-1523

84    *The Annunication*
Wood, 0.40 x 0.36 (15⅞ x 14⅛ in)

National Gallery of Art, Washington
Samuel H. Kress Collection 1939

John Ruskin    English, 1819-1900

85    *Self-Portrait with Blue Neckcloth*
Watercolor, 0.352 x 0.252 (13⅞ x 9¹⁵⁄₁₆ in)

The Pierpont Morgan Library, New York
Gift of the Fellows

Sir Edward Burne-Jones    English, 1833-1898

86 *Page from an Album of Copies* (folio 5, no. 1084),
1859-1862

Pencil and watercolor, 0.286 x 0.229 (11¼ x 9 in)

Fitzwilliam Museum, Cambridge

Sir Edward Burne-Jones    English, 1833-1898

87 *Page from an Album of Copies* (folio 17, no. 1084),
1859-1862

Pencil and watercolor, 0.141 x 0.106  (5⁹⁄₁₆ x 4³⁄₁₆ in)

Fitzwilliam Museum, Cambridge

88 *Charles Eliot Norton,* probably 1880s

Photograph

Anonymous

Harvard University Archives, Cambridge,
Massachusetts

William Rothenstein    English, 1872-1945

89 *Portrait of Walter Pater from "Oxford Characters. A
Series of Lithographs by Will Rothenstein"*
(London-New York, 1896)

Library of Congress, Washington

90 *Note from Walter Pater to Bernard Berenson,*
February 16, 1887

Villa I Tatti, Harvard University Center for
Italian Renaissance Studies, Florence

Walter Pater    English, 1839-1894

91 *The Renaissance* (London, 1888)

Villa I Tatti, Harvard University Center for
Italian Renaissance Studies, Florence

92 *"Nincompoopiana," from "Punch's Almanack" for
1881,* December 13, 1880

Copy photograph by the National Gallery of Art,
Washington

Original volume at Library of Congress,
Washington

Giovanni Girolamo Savoldo    Brescian, active 1508-1548

93 *Portrait of a Knight*

Canvas, 0.883 x 0.734 (34¾ x 28⅞ in)

National Gallery of Art, Washington
Samuel H. Kress Collection 1952

94 *Letter from Bernard Berenson to Mary Berenson,*
October 23, 1890

Villa I Tatti, Harvard University Center for
Italian Renaissance Studies, Florence

95 *Bernard Berenson,* 1891

Photograph

Anonymous

Villa I Tatti, Harvard University Center for
Italian Renaissance Studies, Florence

Bernard Berenson

96 *"Rudiments of Connoisseurship" in "The Study and
Criticism of Italian Art"* (London: George Bell and
Sons, 1902)

National Gallery of Art, Washington

Bernard Berenson

97 *Three Essays in Method* (Oxford: Clarendon Press, 1927)

National Gallery of Art, Washington

Filippino Lippi    Florentine, probably 1457-1504

98 *Tobias and the Angel*

Wood, 0.325 x 0.235 (12⅞ x 9¼ in)

National Gallery of Art, Washington
Samuel H. Kress Collection 1939

Filippino Lippi    Florentine, probably 1457-1504

99 *Pietà*

Wood, 0.175 x 0.337 (6⅞ x 13¼ in)

National Gallery of Art, Washington
Samuel H. Kress Collection 1952

100 *Bernard and Mary Berenson,* 1898

Photograph

Anonymous

Villa I Tatti, Harvard University Center for
Italian Renaissance Studies, Florence

Mary Berenson

101 *Sheet from a Notebook Made in the Veneto,* 1891-1893

Barbara Strachey Halpern, Oxford

Bernard and Mary Berenson

102 *Pages from a Notebook Made in North Italy,* 1892-1893

Barbara Strachey Halpern, Oxford

Mary Logan (Berenson)   American, 1864-1945

103 *Guide to the Italian Pictures at Hampton Court*
(London: A. D. Innes & Co., 1894)

Villa I Tatti, Harvard University Center for
Italian Renaissance Studies, Florence

104 *Pages from "The Venetian Painters of the Renaissance,"*
by Bernard Berenson (New York-London:
G. P. Putnam's Sons, 1895)

Villa I Tatti, Harvard University Center for
Italian Renaissance Studies, Florence

105 *Pages from "Italian Pictures of the Renaissance,"* by
Bernard Berenson (Oxford: Clarendon Press, 1932)

68

National Gallery of Art, Washington

Bernard Berenson

106 *Pages from "Italian Pictures of the Renaissance. A
List of the Principal Artists and Their Works with an
Index of Places. Venetian School,"* vol. 1 (London:
Phaidon Press Ltd., 1957)

National Gallery of Art, Washington

107 *Bernard Berenson in the Borghese Gallery,* 1955
Photograph
David Seymour, Magnum Photos

Villa I Tatti, Harvard University Center for
Italian Renaissance Studies, Florence

108 *Bernard Berenson Examining Photographs,* 1956
Photograph
Anonymous

Villa I Tatti, Harvard University Center for
Italian Renaissance Studies, Florence

109 *The "Fototeca" at Villa I Tatti*
Photograph
Luigi Artini

Villa I Tatti, Harvard University Center for
Italian Renaissance Studies, Florence

Andrea del Castagno   Florentine, 1417/19-1457

110 *Portrait of a Man*
Wood, 0.540 x 0.405 (21¼ x 15⅞ in)

National Gallery of Art, Washington
Andrew W. Mellon Collection 1937

111 *Photograph of Andrea del Castagno's "Portrait of a Man"*

Anonymous

Villa I Tatti, Harvard University Center for
Italian Renaissance Studies, Florence

112 *Annotations on the reverse of a photograph (Andrea
del Castagno's "Portrait of a Man")*

Villa I Tatti, Harvard University Center for
Italian Renaissance Studies, Florence

Raphael   Umbrian, 1483-1520

113 *The Alba Madonna*
Transferred from wood to canvas, diameter 0.945 (37¼ in)

National Gallery of Art, Washington
Andrew W. Mellon Collection 1937

François Joubert   French, 1697-1779

114 *Plate from "Collection of Pictures of W. G. Coesvelt, Esq.
of London"* (London, 1836)

National Gallery of Art, Washington

A. G. Louis Boucher Desnoyers
French, 1779-1859

115 *The Alba Madonna*
Engraving, 0.568 x 0.416 (22⅜ x 18½ in)

National Gallery of Art, Washington

116 *Plate from "The Great Works of Raphael Sanzio,"*
ed. Joseph Cundall (London, 1870)

National Gallery of Art, Washington

117   *The Alba Madonna*
      Carbon print
      Adolphe Braun
      Musée du Louvre, Paris

118   *The Alba Madonna* (detail)
      Carbon print
      Adolphe Braun
      Musée du Louvre, Paris

119   *The Alba Madonna* (detail)
      Carbon print
      Adolphe Braun
      Musée du Louvre, Paris

120   *The Alba Madonna*
      Photograph
      National Gallery of Art, Washington

121   *The Alba Madonna* (detail)
      Photograph
      National Gallery of Art, Washington

122   *The Alba Madonna* (detail)
      Photograph
      National Gallery of Art, Washington

123   *The Alba Madonna*
      Ultraviolet photograph
      National Gallery of Art, Washington

124   *The Alba Madonna*
      Infrared photograph
      National Gallery of Art, Washington

125   *The Alba Madonna*
      X-radiograph photograph
      National Gallery of Art, Washington

126   *The Alba Madonna*
      Color transparency
      National Gallery of Art, Washington